THE PROCI
LYRICS
1987 - 2015

Craig and Charlie Reid have written consistently wonderful words and music across their career to date. These songs are timeless, the lyrics capturing a gamut of human emotions, written with poignancy, honesty and humour.

Their songs feature at weddings, funerals and everything in-between and there is one song, an early celebration of falling head over heels in love that is known the world over and has become a staggering global anthem. There are many others that have gained great popularity in different parts of the planet and then there is a wide cross section of sublime songs embraced by a multitude that has kept up with The Proclaimers ten studio albums and compilation collections released between 1987 and 2015.

Their words read elegantly as prose and this book presents all the lyrics of the 137 songs recorded in this period with a forward by the esteemed screenwriter Richard Curtis and original introduction sleeve notes from 2 more uber fans on their 'Best of' by Matt Lucas and 'Very Best Of' by David Tennant.

COFFEE TABLE

ISBN : 978-0-9931177-0-1

First edition 2014, this second edition 2015

Printed in Britain by
Martins the Printers, Berwick-upon-Tweed

This publication has been designed and published by
Colin Usher of Coffee Table Digital
in association with The Proclaimers, Kenny MacDonald
at Braw Music Management and the relevant music publishers.

www.coffeetabledigital.com

Front & back cover photographs by Murdo MacLeod

THE PROCLAIMERS
LYRICS
1987 - 2015

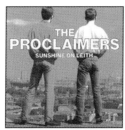

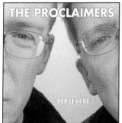

www.proclaimers.co.uk

Foreword *by Richard Curtis, October 2014*

Richard is a writer and director who has spent most of his life listening to pop music. His work includes the films Four Weddings and a Funeral, Notting Hill, Love Actually and About Time, as well as the tv comedies Blackadder, Mr Bean and The Vicar of Dibley. He is also one of the founders of the British charity Comic Relief.

The Proclaimers and Me.

The Proclaimers are brothers who feel like my brothers.

We've grown up together. We couldn't be more different – me England, them Scotland. Me moving pictures, them music that moves. (Though that said – I started wearing glasses when I was 9, and they were born with them on. And I had a reddish tinge in my hair like them, before the white crept up on me.) But we have actually grown up and old together – one of the things I love about them is that their songs have been about a whole adult life. They didn't let themselves get stranded, writing some youthful masterpieces about youth and then trying to do that again and again. They kept watching their lives and over the years they've given me hope, consolation, joy, reflection and partnership, in that strange intimacy which a song in your ear alone can give.

I'm thrilled to write this intro to this book of lyrics – because I think they're great songs and great lyrics. I wonder if you'll let me simply map a story through them – my own version of life with the Proclaimers. What's yours?

When first heard them, of course, love was the main thing on my mind – and they're very good on that subject, they were after all willing to walk the 500 miles. Then I met Emma and even though I never asked the question myself, the Proclaimers did :

When we're old if they ask me how do you define success? I'll say 'you meet a woman and you fall in love and you ask her if she's says yes.'

Simple perfection. Then my Dad died - I was on a plane when he died – when I landed, there were 15 missed calls from my mother. I don't think about him all the time - but when I do, it's just like my Scottish brothers think of theirs...

**Lately, I've been forgetting to keep your memory every day
It's so long since last time I saw you the present gets in the way
But now and then you just walk right in
Ask me how it's been
Since you've been still.
And if I cry
You just smile and sigh
I never said goodbye.
I never will.**

Then my Mum got very sick - we knew she had less than a year. We had time to prepare - time to say all the things that I wanted to say...

The love you leave will be there after you're gone
The air you breathe will be there, after you're gone...

After her death I do indeed believe in eternal life. She's not alive – but she absolutely exists in every piece of my behaviour and her love still is the thing that gives confidence – it is the air that I breathe.

Whatever happens, whatever turn my life takes, the Proclaimers seem to have got there before me. I've been travelling a lot recently – trying to reconcile it with my real life and then one day I was re-listening to Notes and Rhymes....

When I close my eyes I can see
The faces of my family
Three more days and I'm home
Everything that I hold dear
Lies 5 thousands miles from here
Three more days and I'm home

And then sometimes I try to stand back and think back on my life of love and loss and how could I do better than one of the greatest choruses in pop music?

While I'm worth
My room on this earth,
I will be with you

While the chief
Puts Sunshine on Leith,
I'll thank him for his work
And your birth and my birth.

Do I believe in God? No.
Do I believe that the chief puts sunshine on Leith? Yes, I do.

I've only actually met these members of my family a few times – a firm handshake – an obvious decency – solid support for Comic Relief when we asked it. I've seen them in concert once a decade. But I've listened to their music every week of my life and their songs have been these incredible, simple, clear, passionate signposts for what it feels like to be a boyfriend, a son, a father.

You can't separate lyrics from songs – I don't have any favourite lyrics that happen in songs I don't actually like. But when a great song does have great lyrics, it's a peculiar and particular magic and the lyrics are half of that magic – so it's wonderful that this book pays tribute to that other half of the marriage. Reading it explains the songs and sends me back to the songs.

I've chosen to focus on their songs about family and love – because these are the two subjects that have dominated my own work. But there's obviously so many other aspects in this massive body of work, far more than I've covered – every subject they've ever been engaged in, from politics to pronounciation, written with a dazzling mixture of simplicity and wit and perception and honesty and passion, uniquely expressed. Who'd have thought that after all these centuries the 12 most passionate patriotic words ever written would turn out to be **'Bathgate no more Linwood no more Methil no more Irvine no more'**.

I hope this book brings you hours and hours of joy and sends you back to the turntable for years and years more.

Foreword from The Best Of... by Matt Lucas

Released 2002

Recording studio, 2002

If the words I am about to write turn out to be faltering, if I am inarticulate or if the prose is littered with gushing hyperbole, superlatives colliding with clichés, and the end result nonsensical then forgive me. It's just that I find it hard to put into words quite how the music of The Proclaimers makes me feel. I'll have a go...

It makes me laugh. It makes me cry. It just makes me generally euphoric. It moves me - physically - to dance around the room, into furniture, so that I trip and bang my head on the stereo. It makes me sing without reserve at the top of my voice, in my best Scottish accent. It makes me drum, with my bare hands on the table, loudly. It causes arguments (less so now than perhaps when I was at college) that I refuse to lose, that 'Sunshine On Leith' says more to me about my life and the way I feel than anything Morrissey or Cobain ever wrote.

This is soul. Craig and Charlie Reid's music may not sound like anything else you ever heard but it does evoke the same feeling you get when you hear Dexys or Ian Dury or The Housemartins. There is the same immediacy, the same sense of commitment, the same refusal to compromise and the same identification with the material so that the performance and the material becomes one. And like the aforementioned, there is great wit and intelligence. Craig and Charlie's lyrics are frequently emotional, often unashamedly sentimental. Other times their words are as dry and pithy as their melodies are simply divine. They write with unabashed honesty and understated eloquence about what they know best – life, death, love, sex, marriage, parents, kids, football, politics, alcohol and Scotland – and leave the rest, quite happily, to everyone else.

It's 2002. The Proclaimers are back. As I write, The Proclaimers are performing in Dubai, and head over shortly to Australia and New Zealand. Later in the year they will be touring UK, Ireland, Canada and USA again. They have also returned to the studio to lay down three tracks - two self-penned and one cover - that appear on this album. Of course, things are different. Whereas much of 'This Is The Story' was written sitting down together, these days the pair write separately, with Craig the more prolific of the two. Listening again to 'Sunshine On Leith', Charlie, whilst proud that the album is still remembered with affection, confides 'We sound young on it, the voice, the attitude sounds young.' More recently, as their output has slowed, The Proclaimers' profile has been maintained largely by their contributions to various film soundtracks and commercials. They are consistently flattered that their music is used in this way - 'It's kept us in the public eye. It's helped us. We sound different and people are looking for something off the wall.' Similarly, the brothers have a great sense of humour when it comes to the seemingly endless stream of Proclaimers parodies that have appeared over the years, from Little and Large to Bobby Davro to, more recently, Frank Skinner and Harry Hill. Most notably, Craig and Charlie were particularly impressed by Mike Myers and Dana Carvey's efforts on 'Saturday Night Live' - 'They got it just right. They even went to the effort of making themselves whiter' boasts a delighted Charlie.

At forty, the pair note changing fashions. Their kids are into Limp Bizkit, Kylie and WWF. But then, even at the height of their commercial success, The Proclaimers were never fashionable. And do they care? 'We do it for the folk who get the music, who come to the gigs and buy the albums.'

Matt Lucas, March 2002

Video shoot for Spinning Around in The Air, 2012

Foreword from
The Very Best Of
25 Years 1987-2012
by David Tennant

Released 2013

I was 16 when I first saw 'The Proclaimers.'
It was a surprising sight. In the midst of
Channel 4's ultra-hip, ever so cool Friday
night music show 'The Tube.'
For our younger readers; 'The Tube' was
hosted by Jools Holland and Paula Yates
and throughout the 80s introduced the
nation to all that was good, different or
just loud in the popular music scene of the times. Think- the NME on telly.
As a geeky music fan (not cool but determined to know what I should be
listening to in the fruitless hope of passing myself off as not entirely styleless)I
would tune in religiously. I had never seen anything like The Proclaimers.
I'm not sure anyone had. Two blokes, with the same face and a guitar. Belting
out a couple of tunes in thick, unashamed Scottish accents.

Now, the charts were full of Scottish bands in those long ago days. But Simple
Minds didn't sound in the least bit Caledonian on their records. Hipsway were
from Glasgow but their accents weren't. And the only way you knew Hue and
Cry weren't singing live from a smoke filled speakeasy in Vegas was from the
profile piece in that week's Record Mirror.

Pop stars didn't use their own voices to sing. It just wasn't done. They developed
a singing voice somewhere in the middle of the Atlantic. That was just what
happened. And they sang about lurve and gals or they sang songs full of lyrics
that rivalled Laurie Anderson for pretentious obscurity.

But not this pair. Here were songs about being Scottish, songs about car plants
being closed down- Bathgate got a mention on Channel 4. In a song! I was born
in Bathgate. I couldn't believe this. I mean I know it was in reference to Bathgate
becoming a post industrial wasteland but still- it was on telly! Did this mean I
was a little bit cool after all?

Well, not really. Sorry Craig, Sorry Charlie but The Proclaimers have never been
entirely cool. But then maybe that's why they are still here. In the 80s, pop
music was all about the look. The charts were full of folks like Boy George(we
genuinely didn't know if he was a boy or a girl for a-a-ages) David Bowie, Adam
Ant, Cyndi Lauper. The wilder the clothes the bigger the fan club. It was like you
couldn't have a hit unless you were dressed as a camp pirate.
Not this couple.

I am going to go out on a limb and suggest that for that first appearance on
'The Tube' Craig and Charlie didn't employ a stylist.
Just two Scottish blokes singing songs like I had never heard before, and as far
as I was concerned singing directly to me.
Now, in my memory I made my way to Stereo One, Paisley's finest independent
record store, the very next day to purchase the twelve inch single of 'Throw the
R Away', but the internet tells me the dates don't work so I must have endured a

few months of waiting to get my hands on some actual Proclaimers vinyl. (Again, for our younger readers, music used to be pressed on to flat, black plastic round things and in our homes were these machines that you put them on... never mind.)

It still felt like a bit of a gamble investing in this band. At 16 disposable income is hard to come by and I couldn't quite believe that those two songs I'd heard on the TV could really be as special as they had seemed that cold January night.

But when I finally got my hands on that record, it didn't just live up to expectations but there and then, as I played it over and over again, I fell in love with this music and this odd, unstyled, unlikely duo with a passion that has never dimmed to this day.

Nobody else sounds like the Proclaimers and nobody else writes songs like these. Has anyone else even considered writing a song about the honours system like "In Recognition"? Has anyone else ever rhymed "You're worse than crack" with "for you they should bring hanging back" in a love song like Craig and Charlie do in 'Hate My Love'? Or has anyone else ever crafted a song more beautiful than 'Sunshine on Leith'?

We Scots aren't known for our extravagance of emotion, but maybe that's why the passion seems to burst, out of everything that they do with an unruly abandon. The rawness of the accents only adds to the rawness of the sensation.

These songs have been with me through every day of the last 25 years: 'Joyful Kilmarnock Blues' was my teenage anthem, I walked down the aisle to 'Life With You'; every truly great night out I have ever had has included 'I'm Gonna Be(500 Miles)' at some point.

If this is your first experience of The Proclaimers music, I envy you. What a glorious, joyous, blissful journey of discovery you have in front of you. These songs will make you laugh ('O Jean' , 'Role Model'), punch the air ('I'm On My Way', 'There's a Touch') and certainly weep big, salty tears('Act of Remembrance') and you have so much more still to discover. There is a 25 year long back catalogue to get stuck into. So many more brilliant songs to find, try 'Blood on Your Hands', 'Come On Nature', 'Make My Heart Fly' or some of the extraordinary cover versions the boys do so well: "King of the Road' is on here but check out 'I'm Gonna Burn Your Playhouse Down' (still the only riff I can play on the mouthorgan) or '17' or 'Long Gone Lonesome Blues'...Oh I could go on forever. But really my havering isn't remotely relevant. Put on the CD and let the music speak for itself. These songs have been the soundtrack to my life, I only hope you can be so lucky.

David Tennant, May 2013

LYRICS

LYRICS

Album
Hit The Highway all tracks Warner Chappell Music Ltd

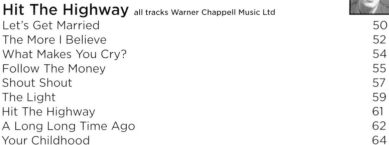

Album
Persevere all tracks Chysalis Music Limited, a BMG Chrysalis company

From
The Best Of ... all tracks Chysalis Music Limited, a BMG Chrysalis company

LYRICS

Album
Born Innocent all tracks Chysalis Music Limited, a BMG Chrysalis company

Album
Restless Soul all tracks Chysalis Music Limited, a BMG Chrysalis company

Title track written for BBC TV Northern Ireland comedy show

LYRICS

Album

Life With You <small>all tracks Chysalis Music Limited, a BMG Chrysalis company</small>

Album

Notes & Rhymes <small>all tracks Hornall Brothers Music Ltd</small>

LYRICS

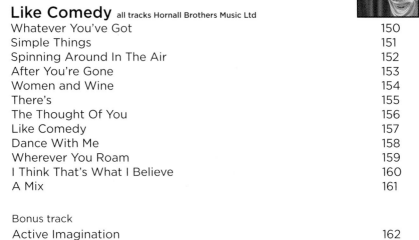

Album

Like Comedy all tracks Hornall Brothers Music Ltd

From

The Very Best Of ... 25 Years 1987 - 2012

Album

Let's Hear It For The Dogs all tracks Hornall Brothers Music Ltd

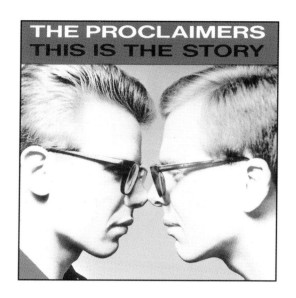

This Is The Story

1987

Throw The 'R' Away

I've been so sad
Since you said my accent was bad
He's worn a frown
This Caledonian clown

I'm just going to have to learn to hesitate
To make sure my words
On your Saxon ears don't grate
But I wouldn't know a single word to say
If I flattened all the vowels
And threw the 'R' away

Some days I stand
On your green and pleasant land
How dare I show face?
When my diction is such a disgrace

You say that if I want to get ahead
The language I use should be left for dead
It doesn't please your ears
And though you tell it like a leg-pull
It seems you're still full of John Bull
You just refuse to hear

Oh what can I do
To be understood by you
Perhaps for some money
I could talk like a bee dripping honey

Warner Chappell Music Ltd

Over and Done With

This is a story of our first teacher
Shetland made her jumpers
And the Devil made her features
Threw up her hands when my mum said our names
Embroidered all her stories with slanderous claims

It's over and done with

This is a story of losing my virginity
I held my breath and the bed held a trinity
People, I'm making no claims to no mystery
Sometimes it feel like my sex life's all history

It's over and done with

I'm not saying these events didn't
Touch our lives in any way
But, ah, they didn't make the impression
That some people say

This is a story of watching a man dying
The subject's unpopular but I don't feel like lying
When I think of it now, I acted like a sinner
I just washed my hands then I went for my dinner

Yeah
It's over and done with

Warner Chappell Music Ltd

Misty Blue

When the inspiration is above my station
Thoughts are melancholy and I let them pass
I tend to view this nation
Through the condensation
On a dirty glass

When the singer solemn was a bonnie laddie
When she brushed his hair with a watered comb
Then he could have dandered
And he could have shown ye
Seven hills like Rome

If misty eyes can witness love and affection
Why does the heart still resist
What the hell is wrong with you?

I've got eyes of misty blue
All the things I want to do
Are all I ever wanted to

As the laddie grew and he looked around him
At the thugs and rapists in their stolen suits
Louder beat the rhythm of his bloody heart
Telling him to shoot

Thoughtless competition
Like a homemade prison
Made him fix his vision
On a certain fate
What's the use in winning all the worlds creation
If you won't create

Warner Chappell Music Ltd

The Part That Really Matters

Don't get me wrong
Don't mind you shouting
Just think your style excludes
The part that really matters

Just grow tired
Of empty minds mouthing
English language courses
While they struggle with the A B C of heart

We've stopped in the middle
Just to talk about the part that really matters
Cos I mean for all your style
I just don't think you get anywhere near to the feeling

And I confess
That all I've learnt
Has been learnt a million times
By every empty heart
That ever felt a song come home

But I'd he happy
When next, I ask the time
If I find I've wasted none of mine
Listening while you wasted all of yours

You wasted all of yours

But don't get me wrong
'Cos I don't mind you shouting
I just think your style excludes
The part that really matters

Warner Chappell Music Ltd

Letter From America

When you go will you send back
A letter from America?
Take a look up the rail track
From Miami to Canada

Broke off from my work the other day
I spent the evening thinking about
All the blood that flowed away
Across the ocean to the second chance
I wonder how it got on when it reached the promised land?

I've looked at the ocean
Tried hard to imagine
The way you felt the day you sailed
From Wester Ross to Nova Scotia
We should have held you
We should have told you
But you know our sense of timing
We always wait too long

Lochaber no more
Sutherland no more
Lewis no more
Skye no more

I wonder my blood
Will you ever return?
To help us kick the life back
To a dying mutual friend
Do we not love her?
Do we not say we love her?
Do we have to roam the world?
To prove how much it hurts?

Bathgate no more
Linwood no more
Methil no more
Irvine no more

Warner Chappell Music Ltd

Sky Takes The Soul

It could be tomorrow or it could be today
When the sky takes the soul
The earth takes the clay

I sometimes wonder, why I pray
When my spirit just drives away
With a faith and a bit of luck
And a half tonne bomb in the back of the truck

Feel the towel, it's wet with sorrow
From the tears we'll shed tomorrow
Don't bring flowers, take a chance
On some graves you should dance

If it's tomorrow or if it's today
I don't say it will be, I just say it may
When I'm on my knees t
To the gates I'll stumble
And plead my case
In a style that's humble

It could be tomorrow, it could be today
When the sky takes the soul
The earth takes the clay

Warner Chappell Music Ltd

It Broke My Heart

Saw a man who was fifty one
He had married daughters and a single son
And he's lost his job as this years begun
And that broke my heart
It broke my heart, it broke my heart

Saw his wife who was fifty-two
She said, she was sure they could make it through
That her single wage would just have to do
And that broke my heart

Talked about it with the family now who
What began in sadness ended up a row
All the guys with the clever mouths
They were saying we should move south

Saw the son who's been gone two weeks
And he's down already with a job to seek
And he's in Kings Cross and there's no one speaking
That broke my heart

Warner Chappell Music Ltd

The First Attack

Since I started being impressed
By the things that move me
All the treasures that I missed
Came back to stand around me

And as I curse the wasted time
I lift my head to say
Thank you God, you gave the strength
That helped me walk away

All the fear and anger
Still stays within my heart
And I can't recall the last time
I imagined they'd depart

But this is what I'm going to do
When they force me to doubt
I'll ask for what I know remains
To help me sing them out

As rays of sun shine through the clouds
And heat the soaking ground
So when we come to sing the shouts
We'll burn the theatres down

Let every disbelieving sneer
That looked me in the back
Turn, come towards us
And feel the first attack

Warner Chappell Music Ltd

Make My Heart Fly

Please don't go rushing by
Stay and make my heart fly
Please don't go rushing by
Stay and make my heart fly

'Cos I never seem to know the time
When you're with me
You can tell it to the birds
I'll tell the bees

Please don't go rushing by
Stay and make my heart fly

I can't do any more
To get inside your door
I can't do any more
Please let me inside your door

Warner Chappell Music Ltd

Beautiful Truth

Beautiful, beautiful, beautiful truth
Don't leave because I can't see you

You know the hours that I passed without you
Every heartbeat that I chose to flout you
And how I felt no shame

I know this problem is of my own making
I know you're giving here and I'm not taking
But please don't leave this place

Don't let me complicate what you made simple
By looking fancy or sounding boastful
Please bring me down

And now that I have said what's on my mind
And it is obvious that I am blind
Please, say you'll stay

Spin me round
Bring me down
Be my sound
But don't leave

Warner Chappell Music Ltd

The Joyful Kilmarnock Blues

I'm not going to talk about doubts and confusion
On a night when I can see with my eyes shut

I've never been to Ayrshire
I hitched down one Saturday
Sixty miles to Kilmarnock
To see Hibernian play
The day was bright and sunny
But the game I won't relay
And there was no Kilmarnock bunnet
To make me want to stay

But I'm not going to talk about it
On a night when I can see with my eyes shut

When I started walking at Wishaw
My eyes obscured my vision
After five miles on my way
I began to learn to listen.....

I walked through the country
I walked through the town
I held my head up
And I didn't look down.....

The question doesn't matter
The answer's always "aye"
The best view of all
Is where the land meets the sky.....

Warner Chappell Music Ltd

I'm Lucky

I'm lucky, I know I'm lucky
You brought me to the girl
And I'm grateful for the way you made it happen
You put such beauty in this world

But I'm ashamed, I'm ashamed of the way I feel sometimes
When the blood rushes to my head it burns
When I think of the boys that she knew before
I feel my happiness turn

I know it's pointless, nothing I can change
I just make myself feel worse
But through all my jealousy one fact remains
I can't accept that someone got there first

I don't care, I don't care if she hates every one of them
I don't care if they hate her back the same
'Cause I love her so much that it's making me ache
And I'm too weak to bear this pain
I'm too weak to bear this pain

Warner Chappell Music Ltd

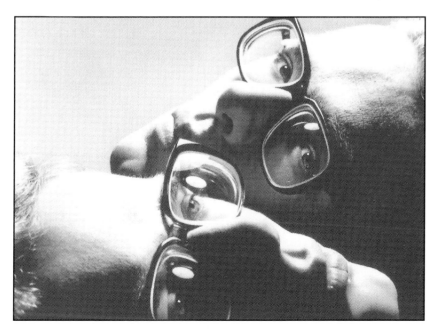

A Train Went Past The Window

A train went past the window
To interrupt the night
The waiting hours of morning
Seemed further from his sight

The wet wall by the playground
Glistened through the rain
And crying seemed as natural
As parents always claim

Silence makes the memory loud
And silence makes me pray
Though empty hearts can beat as loud
As full ones during the day

Sorrow that a desperate man
Can chase away with light
Always finds his spirit weak
When evening turns to night

The Kings Cross train slows down at night
When the sky is dark
Right next to the infant school
Opposite the park

Rain falls down on Abbeyhill
Memories start to shout
As sky and locomotive
Let the tears run out

Warner Chappell Music Ltd

Wish I Could Say

I used to cry the blues
I could only draw or lose
I stored up my hate and I used it as bait
For the people I abused

Teachers who couldn't teach
And preachers who couldn't preach
Who wasted our time on, wasting their breath on people
That they'd never reach

Wish I could say I was better, Wish I could say I was better
I wish that it was true, and it was 'cos of you

I used to know the score
But still say it was more
Then every act or recorded fact
That ever went before

Believe me when I say
I thought I knew the way
To whiten the black and blacken the white
And change the night to day

Wish I could say I was better, Wish I could say I was better
I wish that it was true, and it was 'cos of you

Warner Chappell Music Ltd

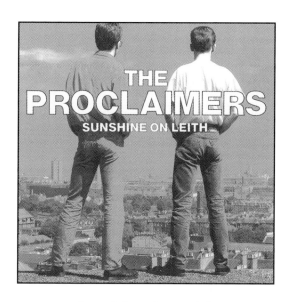

Sunshine On Leith

1988

I'm Gonna Be (500 Miles)

When I wake up yeah I know I'm gonna be
I'm gonna be the man who wakes up next to you
When I go out yeah I know I'm gonna be
I'm gonna be the man who goes along with you

If I get drunk yes I know I'm gonna be
I'm gonna be the man who gets drunk next to you
And if I haver yeah I know I'm gonna be
I'm gonna be the man who's havering to you

But I would walk 500 miles
And I would walk 500 more
Just to be the man who walked 1000 miles
To fall down at your door

When I'm working yes I know I'm gonna be
I'm gonna be the man who's working hard for you
And when the money comes in for the work I'll do
I'll pass almost every penny on to you

When I come home yeah I know I'm gonna be
I'm gonna be the man who comes back home to you
And if I grow old well I know I'm gonna be
I'm gonna be the man who's growing old with you

When I'm lonely yes I know I'm gonna be
I'm gonna be the man whose lonely without you
When I'm dreaming yes I know I'm gonna dream
Dream about the time when I'm with you

Warner Chappell Music Ltd

Cap In Hand

I could tell the meaning of a word like "serene"
I got some 'O' Grades when I was sixteen
I can tell the difference 'tween margarine and butter
I can say "Saskatchewan" without starting to stutter

But I can't understand why we let someone else rule our land
Cap In Hand

I could get a broken jaw from being in a fight
I know its evening when day turns to night
I can understand why Stranraer lie so lowly
They could save a lot of points by signing Hibs' Goalie

But I can't understand why we let someone else rule our land
Cap In Hand

We fight - when they ask us
We boast - then we cower
We beg
For a piece of
What's already ours

Once I thought I could make God a bribe
So I said I was in his lost tribe
Getting handouts can be frustrating
"Get in line son, there's five million waiting"

But I can't understand why we let someone else rule our land
Cap In Hand

Warner Chappell Music Ltd

Then I Met You

Thought that I'd be happy
Going to be so happy
Living life alone
And never sharing anything

Thought that I was finished
Thought that I was complete
Thought that I was whole
Instead of being half of something

Thought that I was growing
Growing older, wiser
Understanding why this world
Held nothing for my spirit

Thought that I was destined
Destined to be nothing
Destined to be nothing
In this world and then I met you

I met you

Thought that God had failed me
Thought my prayers were useless
Thought that he would never give
The chance for me to praise him

Thought the book was written
Thought the game had ended
Thought the song was sung
And I could never sing another

Thought my faith was misplaced
Thought my back was broken
Broken by a weight
That I was never fit to carry

Thought I knew this city
Thought I knew all about it
And then one night I went to Morningside
And you were waiting

Then I met you

Warner Chappell Music Ltd

Sean

Sean I'd say the best one came from Tupelo, Mississippi
I'll tell you now that grown men cry and Irish girls are pretty

Though fear and hurt and care can lead me to despair
I saw why I'm here the morning you appeared

Sean, I sat awhile on clouds to ask God if he's living
I should have spent some time on knees in thanks for what he's given

From parents smart and strong to both of us passed on
From Kings is where you come, through daughters and through sons
Through daughters and through sons

Sean I'd say the best one came from Tupelo, Mississippi
I'll tell you now grown men cry and Irish girls are pretty

Warner Chappell Music Ltd

Sunshine On Leith

My heart was broken, my heart was broken
Sorrow Sorrow Sorrow Sorrow

My heart was broken, my heart was broken
You saw it, you claimed it
You touched it, you saved it

My tears are drying, my tears are drying
Thankyou Thankyou Thankyou Thankyou
My tears are drying, my tears are drying
Your beauty and kindness
Made tears clear my blindness

While I'm worth my room on this earth
I will be with you
While the Chief, puts Sunshine On Leith
I'll thank him for his work
And your birth and my birth

Warner Chappell Music Ltd

Come On Nature

Come on nature, I don't want to read a book or talk about the world
Come on nature, I just want to spend some time being boy to the girl
Come on nature, let me show the way that I've been feeling all along
Come on nature, just because I don't feel weak don't mean I feel so strong

I've been known to ask a few more favours than I should of you
And in time I'm sure I'll still want things that you could never do
If she wasn't mine, if I was stepping out of line
But she's mine and I'm in line and she's the best I've ever seen

Come on nature, let me show the way that I've been feeling all along
Dark brown hair, green eyes and white skin
You perfect every colour that she's in
Come on nature, I don't want to read a book or talk about the world
Come on nature, I just want to spend some time being boy to the girl

Her and me, I could be complete if you could let it be
My desire, is to stretch myself inside her body's fire
If I stumbled in then I could say that I had been
To the chamber where your greatest work of art was on display

Warner Chappell Music Ltd

I'm On My Way

I'm on my way from misery to happiness today
I'm on my way from misery to happiness today
I'm on my way to what I want from this world
And years from now you'll make it to the next world
And everything that you receive up yonder
Is what you gave to me the day I wandered

I took a right, I took a right turning yesterday
I took a right, I took a right turning yesterday
I took the road that brought me to your home town
I took the bus to streets that I could walk down
I walked the streets to find the one I looked for
I climbed the stair that led me to your front door

And now that I don't want for anything
I'd have Al Jolson sing, "I'm sitting on top of the world"

I'll do my best, I'll do my best to do the best I can
I'll do my best, I'll do my best to do the best I can
To keep my feet from jumping from the ground dear
To keep my heart from jumping through my mouth dear
To keep the past, the past and not the present
To try and learn when you teach me a lesson

And now that I don't want for anything
I'd have Al Jolson sing, "I'm sitting on top of the world"

Warner Chappell Music Ltd

What Do You Do?

Yes, I know you're right
I see it in your fierce eyes
But me I've never thought straight
Since the day I had the first doubt
Yes, I know you're right
And I'll back you to a point pal
But I'll never be constrained
By another man's ideas now

I spent too long on this road
Looking for the answers
But poverty and failure
Aren't what I'm after
I painted, "Fight" on factories
But they closed the factory down pal
I want to find out where the heart's gone
Gonna find out where the nerves gone

What do you do
When democracy fails you?
What do you do
When the rest can't see it's true?

Pat votes the Scots way
Just like her mother
But south always takes all
Just like her brother
The next time she might vote
So might the others
But times running out pal
'Cause they're giving up in numbers

What do you do
When democracy's all through?
What do you do
When minority means you?

Warner Chappell Music Ltd

It's Saturday Night

It's Saturday night, I'm feeling on song
I think I'm alright, I know I'm all wrong
The drink that I had three hours ago
Has been joined by fourteen others in a steady flow

So let me walk straight, don't let me feel pain
I'm gonna scratch cars with my key again
'Cos when I go home and fall on my bed
If it doesn't leave my stomach, it'll split my head

Warner Chappell Music Ltd

Teardrops

Teardrops running down your face
Teardrops running down your face
Diamonds of water and salt from your body
Coming down to meet my kisses

Teardrops running down your face
Teardrops running down your face
Staining your skin and my skin and beginning
The stories that you can't begin
The way I feel could be despised but it's a vision that I prize

Teardrops, teardrops
I'm not trying to make you feel pain
Or joy to make the tears flow
But when they roll unashamed they move me so

Teardrops running down your face
Teardrops running down your face
Let me, let me brush them with my fingers
Comfort you and say it's alright
It's so strong this way I feel sometimes, I want to beg or steal
Teardrops, teardrops

Warner Chappell Music Ltd

Oh Jean

I'd never been lucky with girls I confess
Don't know who to blame for my lack of success
Cause even with ones up the back of a bus
There was always the risk of a slap in the puss

But Jean, Oh Jean You let me get lucky with you

The first time I met you it did cross my mind
The next time I saw you there wasn't the time
The third time I saw you I thought that I could
The fourth time I met you I knew that I would

But Jean, you let me get lucky with you

I love her

I want you forever I want you for good
So I'm gonna treat you the way that I should
For your soul and body my heart's gonna pound
Even after the day that I'm laid in the ground

Cause Jean you let me get lucky with you

Love her I love

Warner Chappell Music Ltd

Better Days

Maybe if I just think out loud tonight then I'll know what to do
Five years all felt the same and then it changed and I was loving you
Better days for sure

Mary, our love still can bring violins and roses to my mind
But I swear I haven't missed a moment of the life I've left behind
It's just a fading sound

So be with me while decades turn us older
We've both much love that lasts a whole life through
We could live in Fife or out in Texas
Anywhere, as long as I'm with you

Last year it seemed the things we've worked for were all gonna come to pass
One hit proclaimed that Mrs. Reid's boys would finally pay some tax
Thank the Lord for that

Now I'll admit I wasn't too impressed love
Events compound the doubts I've had before
The only struggle worth it is in the music
The other stuff can't interest me at all

Mary, we've got to see America, I need to ride those trains
This year we're going to take a jet plane there no matter what it takes
For the music's' sake

Warner Chappell Music Ltd

Leaving Home

East Coast trains run slow
And Edinburgh seems cold
For eighteen year olds
Freedom

But Leith feels like New York
All the cars and talk
Moving down the Walk
All day

So I'm lying in this hotel
Hearing sirens and drunken fights
And I paid cash to the angel
Guarding me tonight

Long days on my own
Cry when I come home
Have to carry on
Somehow

Leith could be New York
All the cars and talk
Moving down the Walk
All day

Warner Chappell Music Ltd

King Of The Road EP

1990

Lulu Selling Tea

May I be allowed to voice dissent
Over the Sixties, and what they meant
Cos I've been listening for twenty years
The anecdotes ring in my ears
From people who were over the age of consent

Now I don't recall too much long hair
At least not around where we used to stay
The only guy we thought was okay
Who wore his hair the Beatles way
Was a Belfast boy that Man United played

Mother's Pride on the table, Batman on TV
A Man in a Suitcase, and Daktari and Skippy
Jimmy Clitheroe, Colin Stein, and Lulu selling tea
Going to school in the dark, in the winter

The view from beneath my balaclava
The world from four feet off the floor
Must have had its limitations
Without my adult complications
But I can only report what I saw

And I saw...

Lucky bags, Bazooka Joes, animal tracks on my shoes
I was sooking milk through a straw
in the middle of the morning
Saturday morning pictures, and fireworks getting thrown
Football songs in the shelter in the playground
St Cuthbert's horses pulling the carts of the milkmen

You know, it's funny, but
I don't recall too much long hair

Warner Chappell Music Ltd

Not Ever Warner Chappell Music Ltd

Pretty girl, don't you waste a word
For I can't love you, not ever

Take this afternoon, recall our sexual mood
But, I'm not loving you, not ever

Ooh, ooh, ooh, ooh

See that southern sky
Drifting past the lights
It won't touch you or I, not ever

Ooh, yeah, ooh, ooh

Warner Chappell Music Ltd

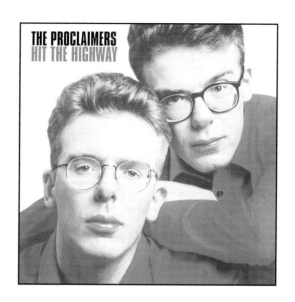

Hit The Highway

1994

Let's Get Married

We've been going together
Too long to be vague
When there's something to say
If it's not now, then it's never
So I'll say it straight out
'Cos I have no doubt, no doubt

Let's get married
I love you and I want to stay with you
Let's get married
Have kids, grow old and grey with you
Let's get married
Hold hands, walk in the park
Let's get married

We know other people
Who drifted apart
Who broke each other's hearts
But we ain't other people
So we'll do things our way
We're gonna be O.K.
Gonna be more than O.K.

Let's get married
We're ready for tying the knot
Let's get married
Set the seal on the feelings we've got
Let's get married
We can make each other happy or we can make each other blue
Yeah, it's just a piece of paper but it says "I Love You"
For the good times
For the days when we can do no wrong
For the bad times
For the moments we think we can't go on
For the family
For the lives of the children that we planned
Let's get married
C'mon darlin', please take my hand

Let's Get Married cont...

And I'll be the one
Who's by your side
I'll be the one
Still taking pride
When we're old if they ask me
"How do you define success?"
I'll say,
"You meet a woman
 You fall in love
 You ask her and
 She says 'Yes'"

Let's get married
I love you and I want to stay with you
Let's get married
Have kids and grow old and grey with you
Let's get married
Hold hands, walk in the park
Alright you can get a cat just as long as it barks
For the good times
For the days when we can do no wrong
For the bad times
For the moments we think we can't go on
For the family
For the lives of the children that we've planned
Let's get married
C'mon darlin', please take my hand

Warner Chappell Music Ltd

The More I Believe

The life that I've been living
From the day I first drew breath
Has been my way of forgetting
I'm on the journey to my death
You make my soul rise up
You make my eyes to see
When I place my faith in you
And I lose my belief in me

The less I believe in me
The more I believe in thee
The less I believe in me
The more I believe in thee

I don't believe in beads or crystals
Instant karma or mother earth
I don't believe that what I think
Makes any difference to what I'm worth
I don't believe in reincarnation
I'm not coming back as a flower
I don't bow my head to kings or priests
'Cos I believe in your higher power

The less I believe in me
The more I believe in thee
The less I believe in me
The more I believe in thee

Oh you've given me a plan
That I don't understand
'Cos I've wandered over half the world
But I've remained an ignorant man
One thing That I know
Is when the final bell tolls
Human love won't be enough
Good deeds can't save my soul

Well I'm not afraid of dying
But I am afraid of you
Because you hear me when I'm lying
And you see the things I do
So the hands go round the clock
As the light goes from the room
And I can't help thinking to myself
I'm going to find out much to soon

The More I Believe cont...

Oh you've given me a plan
That I just don't understand
'Cos I've wandered over half the world
But I've remained a ignorant man
One thing that I know
Is when the final bell tolls
Human love won't be enough
Good deeds can't save my soul

I believe
I believe
I believe
I believe

You make my soul rise up
You make my eyes to see
When I place my faith in you
And I lose my belief in me

The less I believe in me
The more I believe in thee
The less I believe in me
The more I believe in thee

Warner Chappell Music Ltd

What Makes You Cry?

Now I've got a question baby
What makes you cry?
'Cos I haven't seen any water
In the corners of your eyes
For a day, or a week
Or a month or a year
Haven't seen much of you
Since you left me my dear

Can't you see that I'm hurting?
How I'm falling apart
Don't you care about my drinking?
Or my poor lonely heart
I thought you liked football
You didn't mind those videos
And my dog didn't mean
To ruin your clothes (he can't help it)

Now you won't take my phone calls
You sent my letters back
You're paying for a lawyer
To stab me in the back
Then I saw you on the street
You looked happy, that's a fact
I'm impressed - it's a hell of an act

Angel - admit it, admit it
Darlin' - admit it, admit it
Your love for me didn't die
It's just sleeping
And it wakes every night
To your weepin'

Now I hope you can hear me
Wherever you are
In a cheap hotel room
Or the back seat of a car
I make up those situations
I don't know if they're true
But I'll tell you, for now, they'll do

Angel - admit it, admit it etc

Now I've got a question baby
What makes you cry?

Warner Chappell Music Ltd

Follow The Money

I've got to follow the money
Gotta go to work
Gotta make a living
Till my body hurts

Gotta bite my lip
Gotta wreck my health
Gotta break my back
For my share of wealth

I've gotta the follow money
Gotta earn my pay
I spent everything
I earned yesterday

Gotta find the cash
'Cause it won't find me
So I can feed myself
And my family

When I left school I was bummin' around
I'd smoke and drink and let my mind wander
I'd roll out of bed about twelve o'clock
I can't do that any longer

I've gotta follow the money
Gotta go to work
Gotta make a living
Till my body hurts

Gotta bite my lip
Gotta wreck my health
Gotta break my back
For my share of wealth

Now I need to toil 'cause it's good for my soul
I feel clean when I'm working
You drop all the mystical Celtic bull
'Cause that stuff's just jerking

I'm not saying that I work like my dad
I know I don't work like my mum
But I'm made of the same stuff and I'm six feet tall
Gimme the tools, I'll get the job done

continued...

Follow The Money cont...

Gotta follow the money
Gotta go to work
Gotta make a living
Till my body hurts

Gotta bit my lip
Gotta break my back
For my share of wealth

I've gotta follow the money
Gotta earn my pay
I spent everything
I earned yesterday

Gotta find the cash
'Cause it won't find me
So I can feed myself and my family
Feed myself and my family
That's why

I'm working
I'm working
I'm working
I'm working
I'm working
I'm working now

Warner Chappell Music Ltd

Shout Shout

Correct me if you think that I'm mistaken
I wouldn't want to overstate my case
But while I'm the one bringing home the bacon
I've got a right to be heard around this place

You seem to think that life dealt you a bad deal
On the day we both pronounced the words "I do"
You yell at me for hours about what bugs you
Well that's a waste of time 'cos I can do that too

Shout shout don't leave a doubt
Smash up the place or throw things about
You won't change a thing by doing that
Rant, rave pull out your hair
Turn on the tears, I still won't care
You don't move me an inch when you do that

I'm trying my best to be your husband
And a father to our little baby girl
And I'd rather rely on my own judgement
Than the vagaries and fashions of this world

If you wanted a doctor or a lawyer
You should have married one of them instead of me
Or some other guy who would ignore you
When he'd make a point and you would disagree

Shout shout don't leave a doubt
Smash up the place or throw things about
You won't change a thing by doing that
Rant rave pull out your hair
Turn on the tears, I still won't care
You don't move me an inch when you do that

And now I'll make my confession
I love to row as much as you
But while it might be fun, in the long run
It's not going to change a thing we do

continued...

Shout Shout cont...

Again I make my confession
I love to row as much a you
But while it might be fun, in the long run
It's not going to change a thing we do

Shout shout don't leave a doubt
Smash up the place or throw things about
You won't change a thing by doing that
Rant, rave pull out your hair
Turn on the tears, I still won't care
You don't move me an inch when you do that

Shout shout don't leave a doubt
Smash up the place or throw things about
You won't change a thing by doing that
Rant rave pull out your hair
Turn on the tears, I still won't care
You don't move me an inch when you do that

Warner Chappell Music Ltd

The Light

You make it sound easy
You say you just hold your hand out, don't you?
You just hold your hand out, don't you?
That hope never leaves you
'Cos a light shines on that helps you to steer
Makes everything clear
(Well, it might)
Well, it might in your world
(But it doesn't)
But it doesn't in mine
(I've been stumbling)
I've been stumbling in the dark for years
And the light just made me blind

You say, it lights every pathway
Shows me how to live life
For the rest of my days
For the rest of my days
(But I can't)
But I can't put my faith in
(Your words)
Your words and demands
(I believe)
I believe in God alright
It's folk like you, I just can't stand

You don't have to try and scare me
To reinforce my faith, sir
'Cos I know that one day
I'll stand before my maker

(And if I'm found)
And if I'm found wanting
(When my case)
When my case is heard
(It'll be)
It'll be by the author
Not some interpreter of his words

continued...

The Light cont...

You make it sound easy
You say just hold your hand out, don't you?
You just hold your hand out, don't you?
That hope never leaves you
'Cos a light shines on that helps you to steer
Makes everything clear
(Well, it might)
Well, it might in your world
(But it doesn't)
But it doesn't in mine
(I've been stumbling)
I've been stumbling in the dark for years
And the light just made me blind
Oh, the light just made me blind
Yeah, the light just made me blind

Warner Chappell Music Ltd

Hit The Highway

Your way, no way
Do it my way
Or hit the highway
Your way, no way
Do it my way
Or hit the highway

I respect your point of view
You've got your thoughts
I've got mine too
But you'll be out of here
If I don't hear the words I want to hear

Your way, no way
You do it my way
Or you can hit the highway

I've watched you
Backsliding
Then there's trouble
You, your always hiding

Now if I was in your shoes
I might look at me and think
"There's a fool"
But I'm not in your shoes
And I don't have to play
By your set of rules, no no

Your way
Let me tell you that there's no way
No way You do it my way
Or you can hit the highway
Hit it again

Your way, no way
Do it my way
Or hit the highway
I'm stating not negotiating
You want more
There's the door

Warner Chappell Music Ltd

A Long Long Time Ago

Yesterday arrived too quickly
Caught me right off guard
My defence moved in too slowly
Missed it by a yard
I'd just settled down
With a bottle of gin
So I moved on to whisky
And it hit me again

Memories were raining punches
Down on my head
Knocked me into the past so quickly
They almost raised the dead
So I drank some more booze
And it helped me to sleep
Where I dreamed of my youth
And the secrets I keep

Oh, history is a friend of mine
She comes over to my place
And we have a good time
But the memories
She sometimes brings with her
Get out of line
They're out of line

Show me things, I don't want to see
(Wanna see, wanna see, wanna see)
Remind me of who I thought I was gonna be
(Gonna be, gonna be, gonna be)
Take me places I used to go
(Used to go, used to go)
A long, long time ago

When I woke, I remembered nothing
Suppose that's just as well
And although my head was aching
I could hear a bell
So I put on some clothes
And I reached my front door
When I pulled it wide open
She joined me once more

continued...

A Long Long Time Ago cont...

Oh, history is a friend of mine
She comes over to my place
And we have a good time
But the memories
She sometimes brings with her
Get out of line, they're out of line

Show me things, I don't want to see
(Wanna see, wanna see, wanna see)
Remind me of who I thought I was gonna be
(Gonna be, gonna be, gonna be)
Take me places I used to go
(Used to go, used to go)
A long, long time ago
A long, long time ago

Warner Chappell Music Ltd

Your Childhood

From birth to five, you're learning
From five to ten, you're playing
By the time you're fifteen,
You're never wrong
But then you turn around
And it's all gone, your childhood

Now daddy knows what he's saying
You're in my arms and I'm praying
That I'll be given the strength and time
To make yours just as happy as mine
Your childhood

Every morning
Your crying ends my sleep
I kid on, I'm angry
But it's not a feeling I can keep
There's no light outside
I don't care 'cos I know it's true
That in our house
The sun shines out of you
You've got your mother's looks
You're a beautiful little girl
You'll break boys hearts
All over this world
Then one day you'll walk out the door
And I know you'll break mine
You'll break mine

From birth to five, you're learning
From five to ten, you're playing
By the time you're fifteen, you're never wrong
But then you turn around and it's all gone
Your childhood

So you're trying to talk
Any day now you'll walk
You'll be running around
Make me act like a clown
'Cos I live and I breathe
For my little girl
Our little girl
The most important thing is this whole wide world
Now daddy knows what he's saying
You're in my arms and I'm praying
That I'll be given the strength and time
To make yours just as happy as mine,
Your childhood

Warner Chappell Music Ltd

Don't Turn Out Like Your Mother

You're a grown woman
Good at what you do
I'm happy as hell
When I'm alone with you
As you stroke my body
And soothe my brow
With everything
That the law will allow
I pray, "Don't turn out like your mother"

I'm a grown man
Over 21
I've got an ugly face
But I have a lot of fun
So if spill a glass
Or break a dish
I hear your voice
And I make this wish
Please "Don't turn out like your mother"

Don't turn out
Don't turn out
Don't turn out like your mother
I couldn't stand it
And I'll be damned if
I'm gonna live with another

So many women
Give you so much
Civilized ways
And a gentle touch
A different perspective
That's as bright as a button
But then you wake up one morning
And it all counts for nothing
'Cos she's turned into her mother

Don't turn out
Don't turn out
Don't turn out like your mother
I couldn't stand it
And I'll be damned if
I'm gonna live with another

continued...

Don't Turn Out Like Your Mother cont...

It's not the way she looks
It's not the food she cooks
Her kind of indignation
Don't cause me trepidation
But to live with a woman like this
Would take a masochist
Or someone who could get and could stay permanently pissed

You're a grown woman
Good at what you do
I'm happy as hell
When I'm alone with you
As you stroke my body
And soothe my brow
With everything
That the law will allow

And I'm a grown man
I'm over 21,
I've got an ugly face
But I have a lot of fun
So if spill a glass
Or break a dish
Don't get on to me
Like some haranguing witch

Don't turn out like your mother
Don't turn out
Don't turn out
Don't turn out like your mother

I couldn't stand it
And I'll be damned if
I'm gonna live with another

It's not her looks
Or the way she cooks
That wakes me up in a cold sweat
It's just the knowledge
That if it happened
I couldn't drink enough to forget

Don't turn out etc
Don't end up etc

Warner Chappell Music Ltd

Guess Who Won't Beg (B-side)

Guess who won't beg, if you walk out
Guess who won't worry, or have a doubt
Guess who can sleep, won't walk the floor
Guess who'll be laughing as you slam the door
Guess who won't cry, guess who won't moan
Guess who won't beg, guess who won't beg

I thought I loved you, one sunny day
But your personality got in the way
I couldn't stand
Another evening
Of your moaning face
So I hope you're leaving
Guess who won't whine,
Guess who won't groan
Guess who won't beg,
Guess who won't beg

Well, I tried to treat you right
When you said you wanted love
I acted like a tiger
And I acted like a dove
And you say you haven't made up
You claim you haven't made up your mind
But I know you want to leave me
So why don't you just leave me behind
Guess who won't beg

Guess who won't plead,
Or make a fuss
To try and bother
To try and save us
Won't even lie,
Won't even hussle
Won't lift a finger,
Or move a muscle
Won't say he's wrong,
Walk by the door
Guess who won't beg,
Anymore, woah

continued...

Guess Who Won't Beg cont...

Guess who won't beg, if you walk out
Guess who won't worry, or have a doubt
Guess who can sleep, won't walk the floor
Guess who'll be laughing as you slam the door
Guess who won't cry, guess who won't moan
Guess who won't beg, guess who won't beg

I thought I loved you,
One sunny day
But your personality
Got in my way
I couldn't stand another evening of your moaning face
So I hope you're leaving
Guess who won't whine, guess who won't groan
Guess who won't beg, guess who won't beg

Warner Chappell Music Ltd

Bobby (B-side)

He's on his own again
in the middle of the night
He played it wrong again,
Thought he was playing it right

He's on his own again
(There's nothing new in that now)
He played it wrong again
Someday you'll really show how
Someday soon
Bobby's gonna get it right

He had it all worked out
Down to the last detail
But then he opened his mouth
And all his ideas failed

Oh Bobby
Well it can't be love
Cos if that was love
Then you would've wanted to fight
Bobby
Well it can't be love
And even you should see that
Although you're way too bright

He put his best suit on
And spent all his money
He buzzed around the hive
But didn't get the honey

He's on his own again
(There's nothing new in that now)
He played it wrong again
Someday you'll really show how
Someday soon
Bobby's gonna get it right

continued...

Bobby cont...

Oh Bobby
Well it can't be love
Cos if that was love
Then you would've wanted to fight
Bobby
Now it can't be love
And even you should see that
Although you're way too bright

Well he's on his own again
in the middle of the night
He played it wrong again
(Thought he was playing it right)
He's on his own again
(There's nothing new in that now)
He played it wrong again
Someday you'll really show how
Someday soon
Bobby's gonna get it right

Warner Chappell Music Ltd

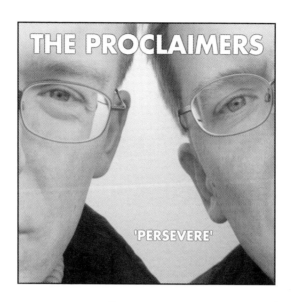

Persevere

2001

There's A Touch

There's a touch upon my lips
Left by memory's fingertips
I still hear her voice
When there's no sound

There's a touch upon my skin
Left when she went back to him
All the rest has gone
She's not around

When I saw her first
It was lust my friend
Thought it would burn
Then it would end
But I lost my old philosophy
Now I believed in love
Well the months went by and my love grew strong
Thought she felt the same but I was wrong
She held my old philosophy
Now I'm destroyed by love

Well I still believed that I would win
Cos I was a better man than him
She held the new philosophy
Now she believed in love
But the love she felt was not for me
Said she would have to set me free
Now I know there's no philosophy
That can't be destroyed by love

Chysalis Music Limited, a BMG Chrysalis company

Sweet Little Girls

Sweet little girls
Cut a swathe through this world
Using skills that they get
From their mothers
Sweet little girls
Might like ribbons and curls
But they most like to torture their brothers

And sweet little girls
Love their friends
'Till it hurts
Or until
They can find them another

Watch their lips, they make a circle like
"Coo coo coo coo"
But the words their saying softly are
Cruel cruel cruel

Yeah sweet little girls
Cut a swathe through this world
Using skills that they get
From their mothers
Using skills that they get from their mothers

Chysalis Music Limited, a BMG Chrysalis company

A Land Fit For Zeros

Hold hands with the person to your right
Hold hands and try to look sincere-o
Tell them, though you don't know their name
That you still can feel their pain
Yeah you still can feel their pain
We'll sing "Jerusalem" now boys
As we build a land fit for zeros
It's all that I can do to stop
Fake tears from welling up
Fake tears from welling up

If you thought this was your country
You can just forget it
You're too old
You're too poor
You're too posh
You'll never get in here wearing that my dear

Don't smoke, don't smack
Don't eat red meat
This is a tolerant land fit for zeros
And if you're lost just hear my call
"Mediocrity is all. Mediocrity is all"

The past is all forgotten now
This is a young, modern land
Fit for zeros
And if we fight, it's only when
We're guaranteed to win
We can be guaranteed to win
And should you, just stray
Just hear my call
"Mediocrity is all. Mediocrity is all"

Chysalis Music Limited, a BMG Chrysalis company

How Many Times

Well, it takes a long time
To find the right woman
The best one there is
Not the best you can do
It takes a long time
To find the right woman
Some men never do

I spent half my life
Lying to girls
Who were looking for love
Where it didn't exist
The rest of the time,
I was worrying myself
About what it was that I'd missed

How many times
I don't know, I don't know
How many times
I don't know but when it happened my heart started to go
Ooh-aah, ooh-aah
Ooh-aah, ooh-aah

I didn't trust you
From the moment I saw you
I didn't trust you
And I know it was right
But my head and my heart,
Have been fighting a battle
And my heart started winning last night

How many times etc

Well, I'm bored by pain and I'm tired of sorrow
Give me the word and I'll leave here tomorrow
I don't give a damn about anything else
The rest of the world can go and hang themselves

Chysalis Music Limited, a BMG Chrysalis company

One Too Many

I think I had one too many
I know I had one too many
I think I had one too many is all

I'm trying hard
But I can't remember
How I got home
Don't recall any streets I roamed
Can't remember at all

I think I had one too many
It must have been the one too many
I think I had one too many is all
To my disgrace
All I recall is my daddy's face
And how I wish
That I could see him again

I think I had one too many
I know I had one too many
I think I had one too many is all

Chysalis Music Limited, a BMG Chrysalis company

That's When He Told Her

Streetlight, yellowing the room
Lifting out her features from the gloom
Singsong, in the street below
Football song that everybody knows

That's when he told her
When he told her that he
That he loved her and he
And he'd love her all his life
That's when he told her
That he loved her
And he'd love her all his life

Bright lights, five years down the line
Point to where the just born baby's crying
He knows now, they are joined for good
Life can never break them, nothing could

That's when he told her etc

Thirty years pass like a sonic boom
Sunlight floods into a different room
They both know they're saying goodbye too soon
But there's no more time

That's when he told her
When he told her that he
That he loved her
And he'd loved her all his life
That's when he told her
That he meant it
When he said he loved her
And he'd love her all his life

Chysalis Music Limited, a BMG Chrysalis company

Scotland's Story

Michael McGrory from west Donegal
You came to Glasgow with nothing at all
You fought the landlord then the Afrika Korps
When you came to Glasgow with nothing at all

Abraham Caplan from Vilnius you came
You were heading for New York but Leith's where you've stayed
You built a great business which benefits all
Since you came to this land with nothing at all

In Scotland's story I read that they came
The Gael and the Pict, the Angle and Dane
But so did the Irishman, Jew and Ukraine
They're all Scotland's story and they're all worth the same

Joseph D'Angelo dreams of the days
When Italian kids in the Grassmarket played
We burned out his shop when the boys went to war
But auld Joe's a big man and he forgave all

In Scotland's story I'm told that they came
The Gael and the Pict, the Angle and Dane
But where's all the Chinese and Indian names?
They're in my lands story and they're all worth the same

Christina McKay, I learned of your name
How you travelled south from Delny one day
You raised a whole family in one room they say
And the X on the line stands in place of your name

So in the old story I'll bet that I came
From Gael and Pict and Angle and Dane
And a poor migrant girl who could not write her name
It's a common old story but it's mine just the same

All through the story the immigrants came
The Gael and the Pict, the Angle and Dane
From Pakistan, England and from the Ukraine
We're all Scotland's story and we're all worth the same
Your Scotland's story is worth just the same

Chysalis Music Limited, a BMG Chrysalis company

When You're In Love

When you're in love
You don't know much about it
Not in your mind,
Romantic love
Rots the brain, no doubt about it
You're out of your mind
You're out of your mind

Seeing things like your heart with wings
Then you hear violin strings playing
Feel all the things that you feel you should
You would lie, you would kill, you would die
At least that's what you're saying
The worst thing is that you really would

When you're in love etc

Six thousand million people in the world
And you say there's just one
The only one, and you must be together
And if they love you the pain is so sweet
And it just gets better and better
And if they don't
You want them more than ever

When you're in love etc

Chysalis Music Limited, a BMG Chrysalis company

She Arouses Me So

Well, it's two-o-one
And she's saying she's done
But I need another go
'Cos she arouses me so
She arouses me so

Yeah, it's three-o-four
And we're lying on the floor
But I need another go
'Cos she arouses me so, she arouses me so

What's the point of sleeping
Instead of keeping' doing it anyhow
Forget about tomorrow, until tomorrow
Let's stay here and now
]
Yeah it's four-nineteen
And it doesn't seem keen
But she needs another go
And she arouses me so, she arouses me so

What's the point of sleeping
Instead of keeping' doing it anyhow
Forget about tomorrow, until tomorrow
Let's stay here and now

Yeah, it's six-o-eight
And we're already late
But we need another go
And she arouses me so, she arouses me so

Chysalis Music Limited, a BMG Chrysalis company

Everybody's A Victim

Everybody's a victim
Seems we're going that way
Everybody's a victim
We're becoming like the U.S.A.
Everybody's a victim
Seems we're going that way
Everybody's a victim
We're becoming like the U.S.A.

I demand recompense
For sitting on the fence
Throughout my adult life
You've got to put my parents in jail
For raising me in Fife
It doesn't matter what I do
You have to say it's alright
And I need you to send somebody around
To tuck me in at night
Because

Everybody's a victim etc

Well, it's not my fault
That I'm positive
I just stuck a needle in my arm
And nobody told me
That sixty a day
Would do me any harm
My liver's shrivelling like a leaf
But it's not the whisky that doo's it
Call me irresponsible
And I'm really going to lose it
Because

Everybody's a victim etc

Wear a ribbon for this
Hug a stranger for that
Light a candle to the dead
And soon you'll forget
That you ever had
A brain inside your head
We value everything the same
We turn it into farce
So we don't know a crisis
'Till it kicks us up the arse
Because

Everybody's a victim etc
Everybody's a victim
Seems we're going that way
Everybody's a victim
We're becoming like the U.S.A.

Chysalis Music Limited, a BMG Chrysalis company

Don't Give It To Me

Your life is full of misery
Well take something for it
Or try to ignore it, don't give it to me
You trapped me in this corner
You're breathing it over me
Next stop's the Royal Infirmary

The room's started spinning
I'm finding it hard to breath
I think I'll have to leave, I need some air
That little black cloud
That follows you everywhere's
Floating my way and it's raining despair

Now I'm not immune to misery myself
But it's just a bore in somebody else
If you weren't allowed to talk of yourself
You would have nothing to say

Your life is full of misery
Well take something for it
Or try to ignore it, don't give it to me

Your life is full of misery
Well take something for it
Or try to ignore it, don't give it to me
You trapped me in this corner
You're breathing it over me
Next stop's the Royal Infirmary

Now I'm not immune etc

Chysalis Music Limited, a BMG Chrysalis company

Heaven Right Now

She's everything
A married man
Should look for in a girl
She's married too
But not to you
And that's part of the thrill
She's the one
Who makes you feel alright
Her alibi's your alibi
it's watertight

She's old enough
To know of love
And know that this is not
But young enough to not be willing
To settle for what she's got

She's the one etc

And if you get caught
You're going to hell
But it's heaven right now

And she's the one
Who makes you feel alright
Her alibi's your alibi
It's watertight

She's everything
A married man
Should look for in a girl
She's married too
But not to you
And that's part of the thrill

She's the one who makes you feel alright
Her alibi's your alibi –
it's watertight

You're going to hell
But it's heaven right now

Chysalis Music Limited, a BMG Chrysalis company

Slowburner

Keep on a slow burner
From Monday till Friday
Keep on a slow burner
And I'll take its place

Stay lonely, for four midnights
Till I'm holding you tight
Keep on a slow burner
And I'll take its place

Keep on a slow burner
From Monday till Friday
Keep on a slow burner
I'll take its place

Work hard now
But not too much
Don't damage your soft touch
Keep on a slow burner
And I'll take its place
Keep on a slow burner etc

Chysalis Music Limited, a BMG Chrysalis company

Act Of Remembrance

Arms of steel, hair of gold
Royal blue eyes, with a rebel soul
You scared me, you still do
But I loved you
More than you ever knew

This is my act of remembrance
My act of remembrance

Doctor's face, said the time had come
I stood up, and began to run
My boy's voice, called your name
You roared back and the silence came

This is my act of remembrance
My act of remembrance

Drove my car, to your street
Hoped a ghost, I would meet
Well that ghost, he's moved on
But his anger, Dad is it gone?
Is the pain gone, is it all gone?

This is my act of remembrance
My act of remembrance

Chysalis Music Limited, a BMG Chrysalis company

They Really Do

They're thinking of you
The folks who love you
Believe when they declare
They really do care.

Though you're demanding
They're understanding.
No need for angst to come
They're captured by your charm.

Palms sweat, teeth grind
You haven't met for a long, long time.
But if they should chance to see you
They'll recall how much they need you.

They're thinking of you
The folks who love you
Believe when they declare
They really do care.

Chysalis Music Limited, a BMG Chrysalis company

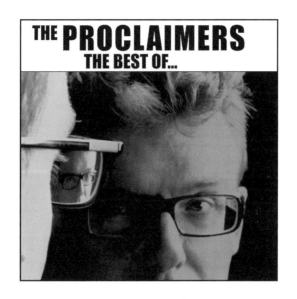

The Best Of ...

2002

Extra Tracks

Ghost Of Love

When you look in my eyes you know that I'm gonna lie
But you look in my eyes for the ghost of love that died
And when you see him you should believe him
He won't deceive you, he's never leavin'
I used to feel the ways he's feelin'

Before I fell for you I thought love was just a rage
But we left the book of love signed in blood on every page
They say it makes you feel so alive
But thats the biggest of all the lies
For every sting part of you dies
So look into my eyes for the ghost of love that died

I don't believe in second chance
Cause thats not love thats just romance
And I know the endin' well in advance
So look into my eyes for the ghost of love that died

Chysalis Music Limited, a BMG Chrysalis company

Lady Luck

I got some bills this morning, they tumbled through the door
I counted every penny but the bills still came to more
And printed in the paper, for Pisces it did say
If you would just be bolder then this might be your day, it said

Lady luck apologises for the way she's been behavin'
And she promises she'll change
If you don't want to know her she'll understand
But if you'd like to take her hand
She could be back at your command

So I ran round the corner the bookies there I entered
Put ten quid on a mare from a stud in Kildare
But though the jockey beat her, in Belgium they will eat her
The tannoy began to rip as I tore up the slip, it said

Lady luck etc

I met a girl this evening and I began to think
That I might get her drunk but she matched me drink for drink
So when she drew the curtains I felt success was certain
But as she kicked me out she spoke in the third person,

Lady luck etc

Chysalis Music Limited, a BMG Chrysalis company

Born Innocent

2003

Born Innocent

We're born innocent found guilty
Living life is treated like a crime
Were born innocent found guilty everytime
Our best never beats our worst
It's as funny as its perverse
Were born innocent found guilty
Everytime

Blame parents blame religion
And the papers and the television
Blame ourselves for causing pain
We love to blame
We ditch the things that make
Us hate ourselves
Just to replace them with something else
Were born innocent found guilty
Everytime

Make claim and counter claim
Bribe the jury but it's still the same
Their verdicts already in
You can't win

We're born innocent found guilty
Living life is treated like a crime
We're born innocent found guilty
Everytime
Our best never beats our worst
It's as funny as it's perverse
We're born innocent found guilty
Everytime

Chysalis Music Limited, a BMG Chrysalis company

Should Have Been Loved

You've been let down messed around
Told to get your feet back on the ground
When you should have been loved, loved, loved
Should have been loved
You've been ripped off, written off
Told an act of kindness made you soft
When you should have been loved, loved, loved
You should have been loved

But all your detractors underestimated you
'Cause they don't know you like I do

You've slept rough, stolen stuff
Been beaten by a guy to show he's tough
When you should have been loved, loved, loved
Should have been loved
And anything new you tried to do
Got treated like a jumper in a queue
When you should have been loved, loved, loved
Should have been loved

But when there was pity and when there was wealth
You wasted neither on yourself

Should have been loved, should have been loved
Should have been loved, should have been loved

Should have been loved, should have been loved
Should have been loved, should have been loved

But all your detractors underestimated you
Cause they don't know you like I do

You've been let down, messed around
Told to get your feet back on the ground
When you should have been loved, loved, loved

Chysalis Music Limited, a BMG Chrysalis company

Blood On Your Hands

There's blood on your hands from somewhere new
Wash it away, wash it away
Blood on your hands from somewhere new
Wash it away, wash it away
There's blood on your hands from somewhere new
Your latest success must be pleasing you
Blood on your hands from somewhere new
Sleep tight

There's blood on your hands from your victims bodies
Wash it away, wash it away
And blood on your hands from your martyrs bodies
Wash it away, wash it away
The blood on your hands from your victims bodies
And the blood on your hands from your martyrs bodies
Looks he same shade of red to me
But sleep tight

But even in your dreams
You can't get your hands clean
Will they clean them in paradise?
Do you think they'll clean them in paradise?

Sleep tight

But even in your dreams
You can't get your hands clean
Will they clean them in paradise?
Do you think they'll clean them in paradise?

There's blood on your hands from somewhere new
Wash it away, wash it away
Blood on your hands from somewhere new
Wash it away, wash it away
There's blood on your hands from somewhere new
Your latest success must be pleasing you
Blood on your hands from somewhere new
Sleep tight, sleep tight, sleep tight tonight

Chysalis Music Limited, a BMG Chrysalis company

Unguarded Moments

These unguarded moments
When you move across the floor
And look in my direction
As I look back in yours
A questions asked a pledge is made
With fire in your eyes
The unguarded moments remind me

Of a picture drawn upon my heart
Before I was 16
And though I'd never met you
It felt real inside the dream
We fought and loved
And fought again
Till all the pain was gone
But these unguarded moments lived on

You take a chance and love someone
There's nothing left to lose
Just let go and give in
Then you'll win, then you'll win

You take a chance and love someone
There's nothing left to lose
Just let go and give in
Then you'll win, then you'll win

These unguarded moments
As you move across the floor

Chysalis Music Limited, a BMG Chrysalis company

Hate My Love

I like the smell of petrol
I love the taste of booze
But I hate my love for you
Yeah I hate my love for you

I like Johnny Cash
Singing "A Boy Named Sue"
But I hate my love for you
Yeah I hate my love for you

You're worse than drink
You're worse than crack
For you they should bring hanging back
And I should be the one to string you up

I hate the sound of cliché
As it begins to call
But I hate my love for you
Most of all

Hate my love for you, hate my love for you

I'd tell your ma
I'd tell your pa
But you don't come from Arkansas
And I can't send you back where you belong

I like the way you're standing
In just your high heeled shoes
But I hate my love for you
Yeah I hate my love my love for you

I hate my love for you
Yeah I hate my love for you

Redeemed

Night has passed away
But I've lived to see another day
And I'm glad that I'm around
Yesterday was bad, don't think I've ever felt so sad
But it left without a sound
The sun came rising up
And it drove away the darkness
The morning air is clean
I'm redeemed, I'm redeemed

Found the strength I lacked
To shake this burden from my back
Between the hours of four and five
And as I fell asleep
I heard the traffic in the street
And felt the joy of being alive
I don't trust myself
So I trust myself to reason
But I feel what it means
I'm redeemed, I'm redeemed

The sun came rising up
And it drove away the darkness
The morning air is clean
I'm redeemed, I'm redeemed
I don't trust myself
So I trust myself to reason
But I feel what it means
I'm redeemed, I'm redeemed

Chysalis Music Limited, a BMG Chrysalis company

You Meant It Then

My fingers hold an old love letter
Written in your hand
Sent to myself, sent to myself
I'll read it now and I'll feel better
And when I can stand
I'll drink to your health, drink to your health
You say that it's a scrap of paper
Dated way back when
But you meant it then, you meant it then

My fingers hold an old love letter
written in your hand
sent to myself, sent to myself
I'll read it now and I'll feel better
And when I can stand
I'll drink to your health, drink to your health
You say that it's a scrap of paper
Dated way back when
But you meant it then, you meant it then

I meant it too
Cause it was true
Tell me I'm wrong, tell me I'm wrong

My memory holds another letter
Written in my hand
sent to yourself, sent to yourself
You tore it to a hundred pieces
And I understand
Cause I was bad for your health, bad for your health
I'll never write another letter
I won't get hurt again
But I meant it then, I meant it then

Chysalis Music Limited, a BMG Chrysalis company

He's Just Like Me

His father's pride, his mother's joy
The end result of love, a beautiful little boy
You think he's perfect, and that he'll be
The answer to the disappointment that you feel in me

But he's just like me
You'll never own him
You won't control him
He'll never phone
You civilise him
And I'll criticise him and along the way
He'll grow to be a man

How many mothers
Gaze on their sons
And hope with all their heart
That he's gonna be the one
Who'll never roam and never stray
Who'll understand women better
Than his daddy does
But all I've got to say is

He's just like me
You'll never own him
You won't control him
He'll never phone
You civilise him
And he'll criticise him and along the way
He'll grow to be a man

And then there'll come a time
With tears and eyes all red when
His girl will say "I blame his mother"
I'll say "no you blame me instead"

Cause he's just like me
You'll never own him
You won't control him
He'll never phone
She civilised him
And I criticised him and along the way
He grew to be your man

He's just like me
You'll never own him
You won't control him
He'll never phone
You civilise him
And I'll criticise him and along the way
He'll grow to be a man

Chysalis Music Limited, a BMG Chrysalis company

Role Model

She's been around for a number of years
Had success with two careers
She gives dying people hope, how does she cope?
She snorts a line of coke before an audience with the Pope
She's a role model for today she is a role model for today
I don't care what you say, she is a role model for today

She's got better looking kids than you
She's got a better looking husband too
She is a sweet little honey, three times a mummy
You wouldn't know it cause she's got a flat little tummy
She's a role model for today, she is a role model for today
I don't care what you say she is a role model for today

But the lady's loved and the lady's cried
And the lady's cried and loved and now
The lady's signed a big book deal
And the story tells you how it all began
In the days when the lady didn't have
The price of her next meal, and its real

There's a secret to her success
She's got balls like the S.A.S.
She's got more balls than me, more balls then you
More balls than all the sweatshops
Making balls for Man U.
She's a role model for today, she is a role model for today
I don't care what you say she is a role model for today

But the lady's loved and the lady's cried
And the lady's cried and loved and now
The lady's signed a big book deal
The story tells you how it all began
In the days when the lady didn't have
The price of her next meal, and its all real

She's a star in every way
She is loved by straights and gays
She's taking water by the sip
A baby on her hip
A little silver ring through her lower set of lips
She's a role model for today, yes girls a role model for today
I don't care what you say she is a role model for today
I don't care what you say she is a role model for today
What you say, she's a role model for today

Chysalis Music Limited, a BMG Chrysalis company

No Witness

No one sees me climbing up those stairs
None to ask what I am doing there
No witness to a soul without a prayer
I never make a sound when I'm going round
And you're not there

In silence under cover of the black
We'll wait until the world has turned its back
Then we let go the vows of old
And the bodies pound on the old home ground
When you're not around

In silence under cover of the black
We'll wait until the world has turned its back
Then we let go the vows of old
And the bodies pound on the old home ground
When you're not around
I have found how that woman sounds
When you're not around
When a tree falls down
Makes the same old sound
When you're not around

Chrysalis Music Limited, a BMG Chrysalis company

Dear Deidre

She's changed her mind on everything
She's changed her mind on everything
She's changed her mind on everything
She's changed her mind on everything

Dear Deidre can you tell me
Where I'm going wrong
I'm following your advice
But my wife's still gone
She left me for my girlfriend
The four faced cows
We had three in a bed
But there's only two now

I wrote to you about it last July
You printed it and millions read Deidre's reply
Dear Deidre can you tell me
Where I'm going wrong
Cause I'm following your advice but my wife's still gone

She's changed her mind on everything and how
She was a mother to our "Sun"
She's a "Guardian" now

Dear Deidre can you tell me
Where I'm going wrong
Cause I'm following your advice
But my wife's still gone

She's changed her mind on everything
She's changed her mind on everything
She's changed her mind on everything
She's changed her mind on everything

Chysalis Music Limited, a BMG Chrysalis company

There's No Doubt

There's no doubt about it now
Youth has gone
It shines upon some other brow
Not this one
Lends its air of carelessness
To another manly breast
Doling out its confidence
To the bright and to the dense
There's no doubt about it now
Youth has gone

There's no doubt about it now
I love you
Much deeper after all the years
We've lived through
Romance is just an old idea
When you've reached your middle years
But love is something to behold
As the old idea unfolds
There's no doubt about it now
I love you

Though age and love rest in my mind
There's something else that I can't find
No I just can't find, no just can't find

There's no doubt about it now
I can't find a reason for existence
In my mind
I feel there must be something else
but maybe I just fool myself
I want to know the God you know
but he never seems to show
There's no doubt about it now
I don't know

Chysalis Music Limited, a BMG Chrysalis company

Restless Soul

2005

When Love Struck You Down

So you're back on top again
Proving everybody wrong
but I recall the days
You didn't feel so strong
When love struck you down
You thought that you were bound to die
From all the pain inside
When love struck you down

When they were handing out the brains
You were at the head of the queue
But once she got inside your heart
They were no use to you
When love struck you down
No one else was fooled
Fear and madness ruled
When love struck you down

You weren't there
When she was everywhere
Her face, her name
But no matter what you said
She never felt the same

When love struck you down
Oh how hard you prayed
But God didn't come to your aid
When love struck you down

When love struck you down
You felt like you were bound to die
From all the pain inside
When love struck you down

When love struck you down
No one else was fooled
Fear and madness ruled
When love struck you down

Chysalis Music Limited, a BMG Chrysalis company

Restless Soul

Drift away let tomorrow have today
While your dreams take tomorrow
They don't fail, even when you fail
Restless soul
It drove you on 25 years ago
It'll drive you tomorrow
It can't stop it'll drive you till you drop
Restless soul

You're always looking for
A place your mind can rest
It's not there, it's not there
You feel like there's a curse
Putting you to the test
But you've been blessed

You're always looking for
A place your mind can rest
It's not there, it's not there
You feel like there's a curse
Putting you to the test
But you've been blessed

So drift away let tomorrow have today
While your dreams take tomorrow
They don't fail even when you fail
Restless soul

Chysalis Music Limited, a BMG Chrysalis company

Turning Away

My jokes don't work any more
I must have told you that one before
'Cause you're turning away
Turning away, turning away

You come and go as you please
I don't make you weak at the knees
And you're turning away
Turning away, turning away

Some love affairs build a love
That lasts for a lifetime
Some love affairs fire a hate
That never burns out

This love affair is dead
Because you are indifferent
You won't say it
But I am left in no doubt

You used to say what you meant
But now you ooze contempt
When you're turning away
Turning away, turning away

Some love affairs build a love
That lasts for a lifetime
And some love affairs fire a hate
That never burns out
This love affair is dead
Because you are indifferent
You won't say it
But I am left in no doubt

That my jokes don't work any more
I must have told you that one before
'Cause you're turning away
Turning away, turning away

Turning away, turning away, turning away

Chysalis Music Limited, a BMG Chrysalis company

I'm Gone

I'm out of my mind
On John Barleycorn
He's such a physician
His fingers are warm
Of my inhibitions
I have been shorn
And I'm gone, gone, gone

All of my fear
And most of my pain
Ran hand in hand to
Catch the last train
From Waverley station
And while I remain
I'm still gone, gone, gone

Ah whisky head
You're mine to take to bed
Ah whisky head

Young women and men
Please listen to me
They tell you that drinking
Can't set you free
Well here I am standing
And I disagree
'Cause I'm gone, gone, gone

I'm out of my mind
On John Barleycorn
He's such a physician
His fingers are warm
Of my inhibitions
I have been shorn
And I'm gone, gone gone
Gone...gone...gone
Gone...gone...gone
Aaaaaaahhhhh

Chysalis Music Limited, a BMG Chrysalis company

That's Better Now

That's better now, much better now
It's easy lying here
Through all that sweat did I forget
How much I love you dear
The tensions all been released
We're slumbering now in peace
So yes somehow, it's better now

I feel it clear in my mind
It seems to work every time
That's better now, much better now
It's easy lying her
Through all that sweat did I forget
How much I love you dear
I feel it clear in my mind
It seems to work every time
So yes, somehow it's better now

Chysalis Music Limited, a BMG Chrysalis company

Every Day I Try

Everyday I try not to lie
But I lie and you're the reason why
Everyday I try not to see
That you're my favourite female company
Everyday I try to regret
The way that I feel
But I can't do it yet
Everyday I try not to lie
Everyday I try not to lie
Everyday I try and everyday I fail

Everyday I try to respect
All the things that all night I reject
Everyday I kid myself on
That today's the day when I'll be strong
Everyday the truth closes in
And I know for sure that I can never win
Everyday I try not to lie
Everyday I try not to lie
Everyday I try and everyday I fail

Well the people all agree
That the truth will set you free
And they tell you to love it
Till the truth has them in chains
And a lie would cause less pain
Then you know you can shove it
Shove it

Everyday I try to regret
The way that I feel
But I can't do it yet
Everyday I try not to lie
Everyday I try not to lie
Everyday I try and everyday I fail

Chysalis Music Limited, a BMG Chrysalis company

He Just Can't

Last night picture of thwarted desire
Is broken, defeated
He's lost all his fire
He knows she won't take him back
No matter how much he begs her
He knows she can't take him back
Aaahh..... he just can't face the fact

Last nights champion of violent emotion
Has cancelled a decade of tender devotion
He knows she won't take him back
No matter how much he begs her
He knows she can't take him back
Aaahh..... he just can't face the fact

Such a way to end
Such a tragedy
Such a waste.....
Waste.....

Last night picture of thwarted desire
Is broken, defeated
He's lost all his fire
He knows she won't take him back
No matter how much he begs her
He knows she can't take him back
No matter how much he tells her he loves her
He knows she can't take him back
Aaahh..... he just can't face the fact
Yeah, Yeah, Yeah, Yeah, Yeah

Chysalis Music Limited, a BMG Chrysalis company

Bound For Your Love

Yeah it's me again
Coming round for your love
The clock says 3 again
And I'm bound for your love
The Cowgate fog won't hide me
But streetlamps serve to guide me
Back into your arms

Yeah it's me again
And I'm down on my knees
Won't be free again
From this love that I feel
So if you hear me pleading
To the God I can't believe in
Don't laugh for too long dear

And the cold night air
Feels this love affair
Even cold night air

So if you hear me pleading
To the God I can't believe in
Don't laugh for too long dear

Chysalis Music Limited, a BMG Chrysalis company

What I Saw In You

I couldn't see, what I once saw
In your lovely face,
Once your lovely face became common place
And the eyes, that are thine
Seemed to lose their shine
As they passed through time
Till they looked like mine

But then last night
I heard your voice
I rubbed my eyes and there and then
That fat baby with an arrow
Stupid cupid struck again

I'd forgotten, every reason
Why I said, "I do"
But now I see what I saw in you

Whoah last night
I heard your voice
I rubbed my eyes and there and then
That fat baby with an arrow
Stupid cupid struck again
I'd forgotten, every reason
Why I said, "I do"
But now I see what I saw in you
Now I see what I saw in you

Chysalis Music Limited, a BMG Chrysalis company

The One Who Loves You Now

Once you stole away with
A new girl to play with
Breaking each and every vow
But she's ageing badly
And you realize sadly
She's the one who loves you now

What became of old love
Love that you gave the shove
Love you called the old sow
Well she's causing hunger
Looking 10 years younger
Than the one who loves you now

So you plumb your shallows
As you murmur 'hello'
Hoping there won't be a row
But she just smiles in pity
At the sagging diddies
Of the one who loves you now

You could do as you please
Find yourself a new squeeze
Make the most of your know how
Or you could just grow up
Give some thanks for your luck
And love the one that loves you now

Chysalis Music Limited, a BMG Chrysalis company

She's Brighter

Her parents are of low wit
But she's brighter than them, she's brighter than them
Spills her words like a poet
She's brighter than them, she's brighter than them

All the men I know agree
She's the finest thing you'll see
But they don't really know it
Cause I'm righter than them
I'm righter than them
I'm righter, righter

Right there in her demeanour
You can feel her soul coming over in waves
Dirtier and cleaner
Than the kind of soul that Jesus saves
What's the matter with this girl
She could claim the whole wide world
But she thinks that obscener
Cause she's brighter than me, she's brighter than me
She's brighter, brighter

Watch her face, look at her eyes
She was born to shame the dawn and the sunrise

Watch her face, look at those eyes
She was born to shame the dawn and the sunrise

Her parents are of low wit
But she's brighter than them, she's brighter than them
Spills her words like a poet
She's brighter than them, much brighter than them

All the men I know agree
She's the finest thing you'll see
But they don't really know it
Cause I'm righter than them, I'm righter than them
She's brighter, brighter

Chysalis Music Limited, a BMG Chrysalis company

D.I.Y

Warmongers, kill yourselves
Demonstrate the power of the product
That you're trying to sell
Gun wavers, shoot yourselves
Make a big hole in your head with a shiny shell

What's wrong with that kind of vision?
What's wrong with that kind of world?
If I suffered less from indecision
I'd stand on that platform myself

Chicken hawks, there's a cell
Down in hell, where you may fight as well

If I may paraphrase John Lennon
Why fill this world with more pain and fear?
To every budding Mark Chapman
I offer these words most sincere

Warmongers, kill yourselves
Demonstrate the power of the product
That you're trying to sell
Gun wavers, shoot yourselves
Make a big hole in your head with a shiny shell

Do it yourself

Chysalis Music Limited, a BMG Chrysalis company

Now and Then

Lately, I've been forgetting
To keep your memory every day
It's so long since last time I saw you
And sometimes the present
Gets in the way
But now and then
You just walk right in
Ask me how it's been
Since you've been still
And if I cry
You just smile and sigh
I never said goodbye
I never will

Lately things have been so good
I with that you could
Be here to see
The beauty of all your grandchildren
By your children
Your legacy

But now and then
You just walk right in
Ask me how it's been
Since you've been still
And if I cry
You just smile and sigh
I never said goodbye
I never will

Lately, I've been forgetting
To keep your memory every day

Chysalis Music Limited, a BMG Chrysalis company

One More Down

Spent the morning - unaware
Spent the daytime - didn't care
Spent the evening - drawing breath
Spent the nightime - fearing death

One more down some more to go
Then I'll know or I won't know
If all the songs I hear you sing
Are everything or anything

Saw a picture I didn't know
Of a football game played 50 years ago
You see the jersey's being worn so proud
But look behind them, look up at the crowd
A sea of heads pointing right up to the sky
Some of them are still with us and some of them have died
I think the one's who've left are still with us as well
'Cause I can hear them when the voices start to swell

One more down one more to go
Then I'll know or I won't know
If all the songs I hear you sing
Are everything or anything

Well I hear you, I don't see you
Yes I hear you but I don't see you
But it won't be long till I'm gone
And then I'll know if my ears or eyes are wrong

Spent the morning - unaware
Spend the daytime - didn't care
Spent the evening - drawing breath
Spent the nightime - fearing death

One more down some more to go
Then I'll know or I won't know
If all the songs I hear you sing
Are everything or anything

One more down some more to go
Then I'll know or I won't know
If all the songs I hear you sing
Are everything or anything

Chysalis Music Limited, a BMG Chrysalis company

Dry Your Eyes
Title track written for BBC TV Northern Ireland comedy show

You didn't have to laugh so long
At my saddest song
That's not nice
Dry your eyes

You have to demonstrate your wit
At my favourite bit
Words suffice
Dry your eyes

Everything I have of worth
Seems to draw your mirth
You're too wise
Dry your eyes

Well I'm glad that I that I amuse you
But I fear someday I'll lose you
To a seizure I've provoked
And anytime I'm going through hell
You say you'll wet yourself
Squeeze those thighs
Dry your eyes

Yes I'm glad that I amuse you
But I fear some day I'll lose you
To a seizure I provoke

And when you see me in the raw
You giggle and guffaw
Cease those sighs
Dry your eyes

Chysalis Music Limited, a BMG Chrysalis company

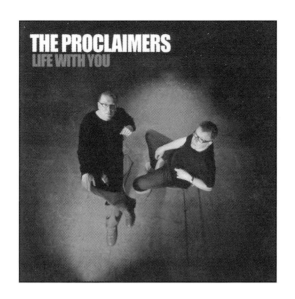

Life With You

2007

Life With You

When I was a younger man
When I was a silly boy
I didn't need a thing, I
Was strong as anything,
I viewed solitude as a joy

But since I met you I'm distraught
You wandered in and now I'm caught
I never thought I would see
Someone so truly good
Someone who's so everything I'm not

I want to spend my life with you
Don't want to live all alone
I can't conceive of the years left to me
Without you in our home

But what if,? what if? what if what?
If it's not perfect then it's not
But every care I'll take
Nothing I won't forsake
To dwell beside what you've got

Every time I think about you
I think I can't live without you
I'll tell you something
I am nothing without you

I want to spend my life with you
Don't want to live all alone
I can't conceive of the years left to me
Without you in our home

Chysalis Music Limited, a BMG Chrysalis company

In Recognition

In recognition of a hundred million album sales
In recognition of your popularity
You take a gaudy prize
From people you said you despise
You wear your self-respect
Upon your bended knee

In spite of all your claims
It looks like you're just the same
As every other clown
Who likes to put the crown
Before or after their name

In recognition of your service
To the working class
In recognition of your party loyalty
You get an ermine robe
And you declare when you are probed
You "only took it so the missus would be pleased"

Oh vanity! it gets them one by one
Patronage and monarchy
And all they entail, rarely fail

In recognition of your bravery upon the stage
In recognition of your bankability
You get to wait in line with soldiers
Crippled by land mines
And you think it's the Yanks
Who don't get irony

Chysalis Music Limited, a BMG Chrysalis company

New Religion

Evidence of a new religion
I'll spare you the details
Effluent from a bloated business
With replica shirt sales
Two for the kids, one for the wife
Indicating a stunted life
Didn't know gullibility was so rife?
Well you do know now?

Evidence of a new religion
Some hippy with a gripe
Strikes a blow with his census form
By summoning "Star Wars" tripe
Here's a thing that I'd love to say
Lynndie England walks free today
If she'll only agree to play
With every Jedi Knight

An Lo! My faith it was honed
We can't be alone
Don't say we're alone

Give me ancestry that's inbred
Give me wit that's completely dead
Give me a zip for the back of my head
I want to join in too

Evidence of a new religion
Meeting a human need
Fertiliser for the brain
Feeding the weakest seeds

Chysalis Music Limited, a BMG Chrysalis company

S-O-R-R-Y

Your prose is elegant
As you demonstrate contempt - it's true
And the targets you attack
Mostly deserve a whack from you
Yes you're entertaining
You fill up the page
Fill it up with your rage

But now there's a doubt
Over the wisdom you hand out - in spades
Please tell us which you think
Is the country we should next help invade
What a bloody carnage
You cheered us into
And the others like you

You never wore a uniform
Unless it was a uniform
Of a school or youth organisation
But for whom watching others do
What they would never do
Holds a sad fascination

And now I'm reminded
By feelings so strong
Of Bernie Taupin's lyric
To Sir Elton's song
Can you say the hardest word?

You demand apologies
From public figures on their knees
As you invite them to say "So long"
So let's hear your rendition
Of words of contrition
For getting it so wrong

Would you like to say something?
Would you like to say sorry?

That's S-O-R-R-Y

Chysalis Music Limited, a BMG Chrysalis company

No One Left To Blame

You're a modern individual
With a mind that's strong and free
And it got you what you wanted
From the day you came to be

But when you got what you wanted
It could never quench your thirst
So you blamed the ones around you
For not warning you first

But now the ones around you
Are going and of no use
Cos as the last one vanishes
She takes the last excuse

There's no one left to blame
You're the cause of your pain

Love made you forget it
Love of every hue
A mother's love, a father's love
A lover's love, a child's love

But it came back again
And you felt like you'd lived through
An almighty deception
Designed just for you

But the almighty deception
Gives while you just take
It's living all around you
While you're holding its wake

There's no one left to blame
You're the cause of your pain

You blamed it on the market
For burdening you with wealth
You blamed it on the whisky
As if it poured itself

Dive into the mystic
So you don't have to think
Find another suspect
Find another shrink

There's no one left to blame
You're the cause of your pain
There's no one left to blame

There's no mystery
Not even the one that you see
There's no mystery
Not even the one that you see

Chysalis Music Limited,
a BMG Chrysalis company

Here It Comes Again

Here is comes again
On the radio, another misogynist,
Calling her a bitch, calling her a whore,
And then he'll use a big word,
Use a big word, some of the time,
Just to make it rhyme,
Just to make it rhyme.

Here it comes again,
Got to keep it real, another hymn to violence,
Suffocating joy, draining all ideals
Another hymn to violence,
Give me silence, some of the time,
Just to make it rhyme,
Just to make it rhyme.

So words are thrown to waste,
And women are debased for fun
And as they start to sing,
I can't help wondering,
What we've become?

Here it comes again,
On my new TV, another well fed schoolboy,
Saying he's a man, but what kind of man,
Puts down women, puts down women,
All the time,
Just to make it rhyme,
Just to make it rhyme?

Chysalis Music Limited, a BMG Chrysalis company

Blood Lying On Snow

You lost your tan
From a few months ago.
Now that red dress
Looks like blood lying on snow.
I feel my pulse start to increase the flow
On this cold, winter's night
With such beauty on show

You don't like winter
You're a summer girl
Sunburned and barefoot
Your body unfurled.
But I can see you're a Celtic princess
And in pale northern lights
You're at your very best

My goodness!
Well, how do you do?
It's taken generations
Of lucky breeding
To make you, to make you

In my life's challenge
You must be first prize
I can see gold in the light of your eyes
My honest soul it just yearns to be free
And I'm sure it would happen,
if you'd lie with me

Chysalis Music Limited, a BMG Chrysalis company

Harness Pain

You need to harness pain
To raise yourself up again
You need to harness pain
And tell the truth about love

You need to break your heart
Before you can really start
You need to break your heart
And tell the truth about love

Then you need to set a goal that you can't reach
Then you have to attack defences you can't breach
Then you need to lose and lose and lose again
If you want to hold the flame
You harness pain, you harness pain

You need to take your doubts
And spread them all about
You need to face your doubt
To tell the truth about love

You know the clichés wrong
Hatred is just as strong
You know it's just as strong
Just as strong as love

So you need to take your hate and doubt and fear
Distil them through your work till they run clear
Till they run right through your art like Highland rain
If you want to hold the flame
You harness pain, you harness pain

Do you want to be the best or be well known?
Do you want to repeat lines or write your own?
Do you want to follow paths or blaze a trail?
When you try to succeed, you'll mostly fail
And you're going to lose and lose and lose again
If you want to hold the flame
You harness pain. you harness pain

Chysalis Music Limited, a BMG Chrysalis company

The Long Haul

The threat - they say
Comes from countries ending 'an'
Where the family name is Khan
And they all read the Koran

The answer - they say
Is to bomb them all to dust
Then in fifty years they just
Might be able to see things our way

We're not barbarians
Like we were way back when
We've learned from history
So we're going round again

I miss the days
When the threat to our position
Didn't come from some religion
But from godless Communism

We're not barbarians
Like we were way back when
We've learned from history
So we get to go round again

Tell your sons
Not to bother with football
Get a backpack on and crawl
We're in this for the long haul

Tell your sons
Not to bother with football
Get a backpack on and crawl
We're in this for the long haul

Chysalis Music Limited, a BMG Chrysalis company

The Lover's Face

She's shackled to the night
Bonded to a darker place
Searching for the lover's face
That haunts her

Listening to the sounds
Of the city as it moves around
Hoping that on sacred ground
She'll find him

And the lover who lurks in the shadows
Cut this hole through her soul
So the children she's leaving tomorrow
Can never be told

Yes, this lover who lurks in the shadows
Cut this hole through her soul
And the children she's leaving tomorrow
Can never be told

She's shackled to the night
Bonded to a darker place
Searching for the lover's face
That haunts her
Searching for the lover's face
That haunts her

Chysalis Music Limited, a BMG Chrysalis company

Calendar On The Wall

Days - no need to count their number
No need to keep a record
Like the calendar on the wall

Days - devoid of all ambition
Sitting in the kitchen
With the calendar on the wall

These are the happy days of boredom
They excite me through and through

Days - when I don't mind admitting
How much I hate the kitten
On the calendar on the wall

These are the happy days of boredom
They excite me through and through

Days - no need to count their number
No need to keep a record
Like the calendar on the wall

Chysalis Music Limited, a BMG Chrysalis company

If There's A God

If there's a God
Where does he go to
When disease and hunger
Knock on a door?

And if there's a God
How does he decide
That she'll be born rich
But he'll be born poor?

I don't know
Can you tell me? Oh
Can you tell me? Oh

If there's a God
Why does he let
People die slowly
Racked by pain?

And if there's a God
Who blesses with children
Why does he steal
Some back again?

I don't know
Can you tell me? Oh
Can you tell me? Oh

If there's a God
Why is he letting
Violence and murder
Be done in his name?

But if there's no God
Why am I lying
Here in the dark
Saying his name?

I don't know
Can you tell me? Oh
Can you tell me? Oh

I don't know
Can you tell me? Oh
Can you tell me? Oh

Chysalis Music Limited, a BMG Chrysalis company

She Wanted Romance

Woman cries in dock and says she did
But she wants the jury to know why she did

She wanted romance
A slow dance
No chance, cause the man she was with
Was Scots not Italian

Woman tells of thoughtlessness and lies
How he bought her panties in the wrong size
So she slept with his best friend whose name was Vince
But then he criticised the mince
Yeah, he criticised the mince

She wanted romance
A slow dance
No chance, cause the man she was with
Was Scots not Italian

Now the Italian men live at home
With their parents till they're forty-one

Woman killed her husband with a sword
Then she told her story to the Daily Record
Which noted how her courage never failed
Until she got to Cornton Vale
Until she got to Cornton Vale

She wanted romance
A slow dance
No chance, cause the man she was with
Was Scots not Italian

Chysalis Music Limited, a BMG Chrysalis company

A Woman's Place

A woman's place was in my home
Sitting, crying on the sofa
Until she'd stop, I'd face the clock
And then I'd fade away

A woman's place was on her own
While I worked, and when I roam
But in my heart, that woman's love
Became everything

You think you know, you think you've learned
From broken hearts and fingers burned
But on the streets in Fife they'd say
A clown finds out the hard way

You'd think they'd know, you'd think they'd learn
From bittered tears and fingers burned
But in this town on any day
A clown finds out the hard way

A woman's place Is here with me
If I can see it, why can't she
But now she's gone, I find she's strong
Well I just fade away, boy, I just fade away

A woman's place, a woman's place, a woman's place.

Chysalis Music Limited, a BMG Chrysalis company

Disgrace

That old idea you're trying to sell
Is ancient, but it rings a bell
You scrub it and it comes up well
But still smells

You wrap that poison up in lace
And sell it on by the case
You still judge people by their race
You disgrace

In a place far from here
Live people whom you hold dear
Who judge you like you're judging them too
They feed you

The more you say, the more I find
To you hatred is never blind
It's colourful and well defined
In your mind.

In a place far from here
Live people whom you hold dear
Who judge you like you're judging them too
They feed you
They feed you

You wrap that poison up in lace
And sell it on by the case
You still judge people by their race
You disgrace
Ah, You disgrace
You disgrace

Chysalis Music Limited, a BMG Chrysalis company

Notes & Rhymes

2009

Notes & Rhymes

Well I'm happy now (yeah I'm happy now)
Don't need a drink to toast our health
Now the sun is out (now the sun is out)
And the rain is falling somewhere else
There is misery somewhere
But I don't know and I don't care
Since you took it from my shoulders

I love rock'n'roll
It took my hand and it touched my soul
You do that as well
You know, you know, you know yourself
But you beat notes and rhymes
Any day, any time

When you walk in the room (when you walk in the room)
You bring in joy and dispel gloom
Your sunny side (your sunny side)
Makes me smile a mile wide
Your charisma is profound
True love follows you around
And lays its head upon your shoulder

I love rock'n'roll
It took my hand and it touched my soul
You do that as well
You know, you know, you know yourself
But you beat notes and rhymes
Any day, any time

I wonder why it's no good without you
Like there's some mystery
When I know the only cure for heartache
Is the woman that I long to see
Standing right in front of me
If we lived a million lives
I would love you every time
And be right there by your shoulder

I love rock'n'roll
It took my hand and it touched my soul
You do that as well
You know, you know, you know yourself
But you beat notes and rhymes
Any day, any time
I love rock'n'roll
It took my hand and it touched my soul
You do that as well
You know, you know, you know yourself
But you beat notes and rhymes
Any day, any time

Hornall Brothers Music Limited

Love Can Move Mountains

A cynical mind
Won't help you through the night
And it can't hold you up
When you're too tired to fight

Where you didn't have the strength
To look after yourself
You find all that you need
For somebody else

Love can move mountains
Love can move mountains
Love can move mountains
Yes it can

That impossible task
You're thinking of
Is one you can complete
When you're driven by love

And the strength that you find
Won't go slipping away
Once it enters your soul
It's reborn every day

Love can move mountains
Love can move mountains
Love can move mountains
Yes it can

So if you're lucky enough to live
To see love come your way
Be thankful every day
That is stays, that it stays

A cynical mind
Won't help you through the night
And it can't hold you up
When you're too tired to fight
But love can move mountains
Love can move mountains
Love can move mountains
Yes it can

Hornall Brothers Music Limited

Three More Days

Three more days and then I'll see
The people who depend on me
Three more days and I'm home

Not long now till I step inside
The place where we all reside
Three more days and I'm home

And life's rolled on and on
The whole time I've been gone

I walk around today feeling alright
I dreamt about each one of them last night
Three more days and I'm home

And life's rolled on and on
The whole time I've been gone

When I close my eyes I can see
The faces of my family
Three more days and I'm home

Everything that I hold dear
Lies five thousand miles from here
Three more days and I'm home

Three more days and I'm home

Home

Hornall Brothers Music Limited

Just Look Now

Wait a moment yet
Have a cigarette
We can stand out here
On the pavement
There's a young man near
With the same idea
And a half-drunk beer as payment
But we turn his offer down
Give him a light and watch him frown
As he weaves his way back round into the crowd

Many years ago
That was us I know
When they said this place was dying
But just look now
Look all around
If you squint you'd swear it was thriving
Now it's we who are in decline
Like the old shipyards and mines
We outlived a time that's long
Passed away

I thought we'd change things
But we didn't change a thing
We didn't change a thing

There's a girl
There's another
That one looks familiar
I think I knew her mother

Wait a moment yet
Have a cigarette
They let us stand out here
On the pavement
Just look now look all around
Now, that's what I call entertainment

Hornall Brothers Music Limited

Like A Flame

I heard the rain
As it skipped and rolled down the pane
Sleep was almost here
But I stirred from not having you near
We were apart
For the first time since you'd claimed my heart
I said your name
And I knew we would burn like a flame

Now twenty years have gone
And I know how much I've done you wrong

I caused you pain
And I know that things can't be the same
But my love has a name
And it's yours and it burns like a flame

Hornall Brothers Music Limited

I Know

You'd lay your life down
For this country
Lay it down for fools like me
I know, I know, I know you would
You'd make the ultimate sacrifice
Lose yourself on the throw of a dice
I know, I know, I know you would

Cos the line you come from stretches back
In an unbroken chain other countries lack
Every single corner of the world
Has seen our banners being unfurled
You won and lost and battled on
Whether the cause was right or wrong
God knows what you do to the enemy
Cos you scare the living hell out of me

He'd lay his life down for his country
He'd like to kill fools like me
I know, I know, I know he would
He'd make the ultimate sacrifice
Blow himself to paradise
I know, I know, I know he would

And the line he comes from stretches back
In an unbroken chain other countries lack
To the farthest corners of the world
Where they watched our banners being unfurled
He's won and lost and battled on
Whether his cause was right or wrong
He's this generations enemy
And he scares the living hell out of me

continued

I Know cont...

No more war? – It's not going to happen
Not while there's men
Willing to fight in them
No more war? – It's not going to happen
Not while there's patriotism
Not while there's patriotism
No more war? - It's not going to happen
Not while there's some
Saying this'll be the last one
No more war? - It's not going to happen
Not while religious nuts
Are willing to spill their guts

Yes the line we come from stretches back
In an unbroken chain no country lacks
To the darkest corner of a cave
Where there's a weapon made to stave
Or gouge or choke or cut and kill
In a hundred years we'll be fighting still
I know, I know, I know, I know we will

Hornall Brothers Music Limited

Shadows Fall

Shadows fall on our lives
So quickly my friend
We feel warmth and see light
Then darkness descends
Shadows fall without warning
And we stumble around
Shadows fall without pity
And there's no peace to be found

Shadows fall on our lives
So slowly my friend
We see them coming for miles
But our happiness we don't defend
Shadows fall where we let them
As neglect turns to regret
Shadows fall – do you never get them?
Ah, you haven't lived long enough yet

Shadows fall on our loved ones
When we're not too blame
And can't see any reason
Why they're carrying all that pain
Shadows fall right on them
But there's light to their left and to their right
So we try to help them step over
But all they see is darkest night

Shadows fall without warning
And we stumble around
Shadows fall without pity
And there's no peace to be found

Hornall Brothers Music Limited

Free Market

Your heart just missed another beat
The grounds still moving neath your feet
Your mouth is dry your eyes are sore
There's nothing certain anymore

You thought that history was dead
Well it just whacked you on the head
It took your money and you're right
It's coming back to take your pride

Golden days are just a memory
But that's alright cos the market
Is still free, the market's free

Survival of the fittest is a swizz
Law of the jungle's what it is
I hope you still think its O.K.
Now its you who are the prey

Golden days are just a memory
But that's alright cos the market
Is still free, the market's free

Free marketeers were on a roll
Rolling in silver and in gold
But then the market grew too cold
So they held out the begging bowl

Golden days are just a memory
But that's alright cos the market
Is still free, the market's free

Golden days are just a memory
But that's alright cos the market
Is still free, the market's free

You thought that history was dead
You thought that history was dead

Hornall Brothers Music Limited

Wages Of Sin

I woke at four this morning
I couldn't sleep another wink
I need to do something
I've had too long to sit and think

And I hope and I pray
That the wages of sin
Aren't paid today

I've led an average life
I've told the truth and I have lied
But I need a few more years
To help build up the credit side

So I hope and I pray
That the wages of sin
Aren't paid today

Yeah I hope and I pray
That the wages of sin
Aren't paid today

Yeah I hope and I pray
That the wages of sin
Aren't paid today

Yeah I hope and I pray
That the wages of sin
Aren't paid today

Hornall Brothers Music Limited

On Causewayside

Did they build this tenement
With stone from Fife
Does it have a memory?
Of an earlier life
Before it was transported
To be cut with pride
And built up till it looked down
On Causewayside

At the edge of the pavement
There stands a girl
Of no more than three
Years in this World
Looking up at her mother
With sheer delight
For a moment
On Causewayside

The rats in the sewer
And the autumn sky
Stand still for a moment
And so do I
As we touch the eternal
Then the cold winds sigh
And blow it away
Down Causewayside

Hornall Brothers Music Limited

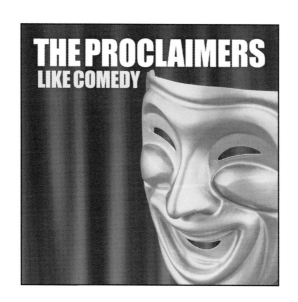

Like Comedy

2012

Whatever You've Got

Whatever you've got
I want some too
Whatever you're drinking
I'll drink with you
You're saying "azure"
I'm feeling blue
That's no lie

Whatever was done
Unto your hair
Vidal Sassoon
Was standing there
He fought the fascists
Keep him in your prayers
That's no lie

Whatever the time
Whatever the place
Whatever the rhyme
Whatever the reason
I'm giving offence
And with your defence
I think we could have
A very good season

Whatever the rights
I want the wrongs
Whatever you're food
Let's hear the gong
We've spoken the truth for so long
We need lies

Whatever the time
Whatever the place
Whatever the rhyme
Whatever the reason
I'm giving offence
And with your defence
I think we could have
A very good season

Whatever the rights
I want the wrongs
Whatever you're food
Let's hear the gong
We've spoken the truth for so long
We need lies

Hornall Brothers Music Limited

Simple Things

You and I we are simple things
Oh simple things we are
Feel the sun and all the joy it brings
To the simple things we are
Water rushing from a spring
Is the simple thing we are

But any hour of any day there is wonder
In all our striving
And our courage
And our thunder

You and I we are simple things
Oh simple things we are

At any hour of any day there is wonder
In all our skiving
And our cowardice
And our lying
And our blunders

You and I we are simple things
Oh simple things we are

Hornall Brothers Music Limited

Spinning Around In The Air

Let me give praise to your sparkling eyes
And your coloured hair
Let me spend ages on poetic phrases
To show I care
Let me go grazing on dappled green pastures
Where you're the mare
Let me rephrase that
I think there's a better line there
Spinning around in the air

Let me donate something to a kid's charity
Of your choice
For you I would willingly be a worse traitor
Than William Joyce
If I could sing I would sing you a song
In Sam Cooke's voice
Let me rephrase that
I think there's a better line there
Spinning around in the air

Are you happy now?
Say yeah yeah yeah
Are you really happy now?
Say yeah yeah yeah
Tell me where it hurts
It hurts there and there and there
Adverbs and nouns
Juicy and round
Spinning around in the air

Madam Onassis took Ari's old glasses
And put them on
She said "I see ships" and she started to quip
About old Boston
I climbed over her just to climb upon you
What did I do wrong
Let me rephrase that
I think there's a better line there
Spinning around in the air

Hornall Brothers Music Limited

After You're Gone

The love you leave
Will be there after your gone
Will be there after your gone
Still be there after your gone

The air you breathe
Will be there after your gone
Will be there after your gone
Still be there after your gone

The lochs and seas
Will be there after your gone
Will be there after your gone
Still be there after your gone

Three score years and ten of joy and pain
Adds up to mayflys on the windowpane
The windowpane

The mystery will be there after your gone
Will be there after your gone
Still be there after your gone
The lochs and seas
Will be there after your gone
Will be there after your gone
Still be there after your gone
Gone

Hornall Brothers Music Limited

Women and Wine

A hundred years ago
I thought happiness was ice cream and football
But time went by so fast
Till I couldn't see their attractions at all
I looked around for other pleasures
The old man had shown the way then
Just in time I found women and wine

I marvelled at the way they united men
From the working and middle and upper classes
You didn't need any brains
Just a taste for booze and an eye for lassies
I'm not basking in reflected glory
But open any book and I think you'll find that
The greatest men of all time
Loved women and wine
Or men and wine

Ah they'll be the death of you
If something else doesn't get you first

Well I'm older now
And have to take my pleasures in moderation
Least that's what it says here in this guide
To declining years in declining nations
But just cos I've slowed up a bit
Doesn't mean I can't cheer from the touchline
Hope sons of mine
Spend lots of time
On women and wine
Women and wine

Hornall Brothers Music Limited

There's

There's your coat upon my back
There's the irony I lack
There's the vapour from your mouth
There's the rain spreading from the south

There's the castle on the hill
There's my final act of will
There's a bus stop in Tollcross
There's no memory I've lost
Memories never lost

There's you lying on the quilt
There's your west of Scotland lilt
Singing me your guilt

There's your voice on the phone
There's your voice on the phone
There's your voice on the phone
There's your voice on the phone
There's your voice on the phone
There's your voice on the phone

There's the snow in January
There's the beauty that you see
There's you walking down the street
Children running round your feet
There's you and there's me

Hornall Brothers Music Limited

The Thought Of You

The thought of you
Precious and clear
Drives all the rest
From out of here
The thought of you
Just won't wait
It rises up
It elevates

The thought of you
Heals me again
Of all the poison
That lies within
The thought of you
Reaches inside
Takes it away
Conquers my pride

Just the thought of you
And time and space and death
Just don't exist
Just the thought of you
And I know
I need nothing more than this

The thought of you
Makes me complete
Wraps all the bandages
Round my feet
The thought of you
Still cracks me up
Laughs in my face
Fills up my cup

The thought of you
Sustains me still
And evermore
It always will
Oh it always will

Hornall Brothers Music Limited

Like Comedy

You were built to last a lifetime
Just not the life that you live
You don't have to make it worse
'Cos the world isn't perfect
And you don't need to give a toss
But you'd make it better if you did
You did you did you did

You were made to be loving
Not a source of bitterness and hate
And when you turn them on yourself
You make one more useless martyr
Make the best of here and now
Heaven or hell can wait
They'll wait they'll wait let them wait

When you lose your appetite for self-destruction
You can stop viewing life as tragedy
Give it a few more years and look from this angle
Where it looks more and more and more like comedy
Where it looks more and more and more like comedy

Oh you were made to be happy
Not mired in sorrow and regret
Misery comes around enough
You don't need to invite him
And when he leaves you should grab
All the joy you can get
You can get you can get you can get

When you lose your appetite for self-destruction
You can stop viewing life as tragedy
Give it a few more years and look from this angle
Where it looks more and more and more like comedy
Yeah it looks more and more and more like comedy
Like comedy
Like comedy
Like comedy

Hornall Brothers Music Limited

Dance With Me

Music sounds through the room
And you take a stance
Moving a tiny wee bit
Like you want to dance

Do you want to dance?
Do you want to dance?
And be held tenderly
Do you want to dance?
Do you want to dance?
Want to dance with me

My eyes rest on your hips
And the way they sway
I'm sure if I held you tight
I could move your way

Do you want to dance?
Do you want to dance?
And be held tenderly
Do you want to dance?
Do you want to dance?
Want to dance with me

Ooh it would be ecstasy
Holding you against me

Now we move round the floor
But not too far
I guide you under the light
That shows how beautiful you are

Do you want to dance?
Do you want to dance?
And be held tenderly
Do you want to dance?
Do you want to dance?
Want to dance with me

Hornall Brothers Music Limited

Wherever You Roam

I could say you never need to doubt
Lie and say you only need to shout
But life can chew you up and spit you out
Life can chew you up and spit you out

And I'm not going to be there
And you won't always take care
But my love goes with you
Wherever you roam

I picture you all around ten
But now you've grown to women and to men
Things will never be the same again
Things can never be the same again

And I'm not going to be there
And you won't always take care
But my love goes with you
Wherever you roam
No matter where you are in the world
You're still my boys
And you're still my girls
And my love goes with you
Wherever you roam

Ooh ooh sometimes this life's unkind
Ooh ooh sometimes this life's unkind
It can take your mind
Take your mind and it'll test you
Again again again again again
And again again again again

And I'm not going to be there
And you won't always take care
But my love goes with you
Wherever you roam
No matter where you are in the world
You're still my boys
And you're still my girls
And my love goes with you
Wherever you roam
Wherever you roam
Roam

Hornall Brothers Music Limited

I Think That's What I Believe

They say, "don't stop believing"
Give no room to reason
Build it and they will come
I've no quibble with that drivel
It's alright for some
But I was born in a European nation
In the twentieth century
And what I've seen and what I've learned
Mean it's not right for me

The say "don't stop believing"
'Cos if you stop believing
Very soon you'll regret it
But what they believe
Is you can believe
And still end up in a fiery pit
So I sit in this European nation
In the twenty-first century
And I know someone's got it wrong
Is it them or is it me?

During the deepest darkest night
I feel that they must be right
But when I see the morning light
Science wins again

They say, "don't stop believing"
'Cos if you just believe
Your future's like the shining sun
I say I would believe
But there's all these beliefs
What if I pick the wrong one?
When I look at the European nations
Down through the centuries
Every single belief system, ended up causing grief, incalculable grief
And if you ask me now
I think that's what I believe

Hornall Brothers Music Limited

A Mix

A mix of pain and happiness
Surround us even now
A mix of pain and happiness
I don't know why or how
It's still here
It's outlasted every year
We're still here
Just like you say

A mix of pain and happiness
Between a woman and a man
A mix of pain and happiness
Replaced every plan
Love is true
Or it is between me and you
Love is all
I have to say

I saw your face I heard your voice
I was a prisoner I had no choice

A mix of pain and happiness
Tumbles us downhill
A mix of pain and happiness
Takes us where it will
It can't last
It's over much too fast
Let it last
Another day

Hornall Brothers Music Limited

Active Imagination

I was down in the doldrums, as they doled out the rum
When they asked me to leave there for making that pun.
Active Imagination, oh I love you yes indeed.
Active imagination, never take that away from me.
Active imagination, ah ah.

I went round to the library, where I took up my pen
And I rewrote the Bible but I left the Koran.
Active Imagination, oh I love you yes indeed.
Active imagination, never take that away from me.
Active imagination, ah ah.

You can make it simple,
It doesn't need to be profound, no, no, no.
It's the main thing that divides us
From the beasts who still crawl on the ground.

I've a strong sense of triumph, though my team, they got beat
And the door slammed in my face means she loves me.
Now the weekend's complete.
Active Imagination, oh I love you yes indeed.
Active imagination, never take that away from me.
Active imagination, ah ah.

Hornall Brothers Music Limited

The Very Best Of

2013

Extra Track

Not Cynical

Glowing
How come you still look young?
You are glowing
How come you still look young?
How come you still look young?
How come you still look young?

Fighting
Life didn't get you yet
You're still fighting
Life didn't get you yet
Life didn't get you yet
Life didn't get you yet

Where there's a problem
You're always asked
You draw a new breath
And you get on with the task
And I love you
I love you
I love you

Laughing
You've already won the day
You are laughing and
You've already won the day
The best thing about you
Is you're not cynical
You keep an open mind and a strong will
You spent losing hours
But you've never grown sour
And just cos you couldn't
You know someone still could

Where there's is a problem
You're always asked
You draw a new breath
And you get on with the task
And I love you
I love you
I love you

You're not cynical
You're not cynical
You're not sour at all
You're not cynical
You kept your wits
But you've never grown bitter
You kept your wits
But you've never grown bitter
You're not cynical
You're not cynical
You're not sour at all
You're not cynical

Hornall Brothers Music Limited

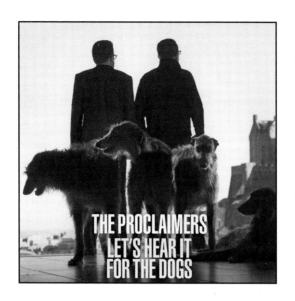

Let's Hear It For The Dogs

2015

You Built Me Up

Yesterday was all black
And I fell into despair
I fell into despair

The whole world was on my back
And my knees began to go
And my legs began to bow

But last night you built me up again
You made me feel that I could win
Last night you built me up again

Yesterday was all wrong
And I couldn't make it right
I could not make it right

But your bravery's like a lion's
Your reasoning myth-defying
You cut right through to the heart of it
You let me believe that I thought of it
Then despair was replaced by energy

Yesterday was all black
And I fell into despair
I fell into despair

But last night you built me up again
You made me feel that I could win
Last night you built me up again

Last night you built me up again
You made me feel that I could win
Last night you built me up again

Hornall Brothers Music Limited

166

Be With Me

I don't try to be the one
Who rains or snows on all your fun
Believe it or not, it's easy done
I do it everyday

You don't have to be nineteen
To be a slave to hopeless dreams
Or hang your soul from rotten beams
I do it everyway

I can see you're not like me
You take your time
And you weigh things carefully
But I can see you're just like me
You've got a nasty streak
Running through your empathy

This is going to end in pain
I'll curse the day I learned your name
And watch the days roll down the drain
And love you anyway

Now it's turning serious
That'll be the death of us
I'm frightened of the way I feel
I'm writing this, I know it's real
You beckon me towards catastrophe

Be with me brightest one
You've got a light round you
Like you stole the sun
Be with me pretty one
I gaze on you and I'm overcome
Come along with me
You've got to see
How you break my heart
With your sanity

Please be with me

Hornall Brothers Music Limited

In My Home

In my home
All alone
The things I flee always find me
But they can tell
All is well
'Cos truth and lies never bind me

And I know, sweet love
Is gentle and tough
But for me, sweet love
Was never enough

In my home
All alone
The things I flee always find me

And I know, sweet love
Is gentle and tough
But for me, sweet love
Was never enough

In my home
All alone
The things I flee always find me
But they can tell
All is well
'Cos truth and lies never bind me

Truth and lies never bind me

Hornall Brothers Music Limited

Tuesday Afternoon

The time was twenty past
Our meeting was delayed
I watched you move
Over Edinburgh concrete
I hid behind the wall
And as you approached
I tried to guess
At what you were thinking
Then memory, took me away
Two miles from here
And three decades ago
Then all at once, so soon
You were inside the room
And that was Tuesday afternoon

This love is old and new
This love is happening now
This love is mine
and I give it you gladly
If you don't want it, say
I'll take it away
And put it back in the place
Where I found it
And every now and then
I'll take it out again
Turn it in my hands
And look upon its madness
Then lead it from the room
And show it to the moon
And remember Tuesday afternoon

I remember Tuesday afternoon
I recall the sweet scent of your skin
And if I try hard I begin
Almost to draw a trace
Of your glistening lips upon my face

I never regret you
But sometimes I forget you
Like when I'm tired
And I make bad decisions
But you come back to me
Your lovely melody
Sings to my soul
And lifts me to heaven
And as I'm rising up
A yellow buttercup
Illuminates your chin
And causes gentle laughter
Yours is the song I croon
I know I'll see you soon
I love you, Tuesday afternoon

Hornall Brothers Music Limited

Then Again

Then is here again
It's never been away so don't call it a comeback
Happy days of yore are all destroyed
And now it's looking like a sad sack

I can't believe that I couldn't see
How many dodgy men were on the TV
While I was growing to a man
They took advantage of the fans

When I was a boy
They were stars of prime time television
But circumstances change
And some of them ended up in prison

Now, when they re-run Top Of The Pops
Some of the hosts have got the chop
I'm sleeping soundly in my bed
'Cos Jimmy Savile's still dead

The swinging seventies
Used to sit on celebrities knees
The nineteen seventies
Sat on celebrities knees

Speculation began to roam
Like M.P.'s through a children's home
"How many more", "what did they do"
Where were the girls and boys in blue?

Now the victims and their families
Have retrospective apologies
They're told, that was then
It isn't now
We've slaughtered all those sacred cows

Then is here again
It's never been away so don't call it a comeback
Happy days of yore are all destroyed
And now it's looking like a sad sack

It's then again
Then again

Hornall Brothers Music Limited

What School?

I like dogs and I like people
Especially the Scottish kind
But Scottish dogs have an in-built advantage
Over Scottish humankind

A wagging tail
And a little wet nose
Can find new love
Or avoid potential foes

But in this small ancient nation
We gather information
In slower ways
And worser ways
Some do appraise by using this phrase

"What school did you go to?"
Sounds like
"Where did you spend your teenage days?"
But "what school did you go to?"
Doesn't mean what it says

Plant and Page wrote
"A Stairway To Heaven"
I don't like rock but that's genius
And in that song Percy sings
"Sometimes words have two meanings"
My God, he didn't know how right he was

Now I know he's a big Wolves fan
But does he favour rebel songs
Or marching flute bands?

On the west side of this country
To stop it getting funky
As they extend the hand
They'll say like Kissinger or Talleyrand

"What school did you go to?"
Sounds like
"Where did you spend your teenage days?"
But "what school did you go to?"
Doesn't mean what it says

Let's hear it for the dogs
Sniffin lickin
Let's hear it for the dogs
Sniffin lickin
Sniffin lickin
Sniffin lickin
Sniffin lickin
Sniffin lickin
Sniffin lickin

"What school did you go to?"
Sounds like
"Where did you spend your teenage days?"
But "what school did you go to?"
Doesn't mean what it says

Hornall Brothers Music Limited

If I'm Still Around

And so we meet again
So we meet again
My young learned friend
Did you mean to take this path?
'Cos I meant to take this path
I know it makes you laugh

I know it makes you laugh
When we meet here on this path
So I choose to take this path
And you choose to take this path

Does beauty fill your world?
Does beauty fill your world?
My beautiful girl
'Cos I can see the world
I can see the world
When I watch you swirl

Does beauty fill your world?
My beautiful girl
'Cos I can see the world
When I watch you swirl

You're dancing rings round me
You're dancing rings round me
I think we both agree
So I lie here on the floor
I lie here on the floor
So I can watch you more

You're dancing rings round me
I think we both agree
So I lie here on the floor
So I can watch you more

Ten years from today
Ten years from today
You'll be far away
And if I'm still around
If I'm still around
I'll walk this blessed ground

Ten years from today
You'll be far away
And if I'm still around
I'll walk this blessed ground

If I'm still, if I'm still
If I'm still, if I'm still around

If I'm still, if I'm still
If I'm still, if I'm still around

Hornall Brothers Music Limited

The Other Side

Just walked through the door
Selfish to the core
Here's the other side of me
Telling easy lies
Making women cry
Here's the other side of me

I'm in love again
Wreck the world again
I'm so happy to be free
Weak as water though
Is the place I go
On the other side of me

So I sit very still
And I'm laughing
As I feel my free will take
A thrashing

So I sit very still
And I'm laughing
As I feel my free will
Take a thrashing

Just walked through the door
Selfish to the core
Here's the other side of me
Telling easy lies
Making women cry
Here's the other side of me

I'm in love again
Wreck the world again
I'm so happy to be free
Weak as water though
Is the place I go
I'm in love again
So wreck the world again
Just walk through the door
Selfish to the core

So I sit very still
And I'm laughing
As I feel my free will
Take a thrashing

Hornall Brothers Music Limited

Forever Young

And I am what I am
And I am what I'm not
And I think I'm a good friend to ye
And I'm not a debauched old roué

Spend some more time with me
And you'll like it a lot
I can bore you with advice
And you can make me feel
That I'm forever young
(Forever young forever young)
I can kid myself that I'm
Forever young

You see the trouble with me
I've got some years on the clock
But the magic in your hands is
Much cheaper than monkey glands is

And you do what you want to do
And you say what you want to say
And everything you do and say is OK

And I am what I am
And I am what I'm not
And I think I'm a good friend to ye
And I'm not debauched old rue

Spend some more time with me
And you'll like it a lot
I can bore you with advice
And you can make me feel
That I'm forever young
(Forever young forever young)
You can make me feel that
I'm forever young
I can kid myself that I'm forever young
Delude myself that I was ever young
Forever young

Hornall Brothers Music Limited

Ten Tiny Fingers

Ten tiny fingers, ten tiny toes
I thought I knew about love
But I didn't know
No no, I didn't know

My newborn daughter
Lay in my arms
And I was a fool for all her charms
But no no no, I didn't know

I was a patsy, I was a dupe
I couldn't think
My brains had turned to soup
I couldn't speak, but my heart
Began to whoop
It's the age-old story

Ten tiny fingers, ten tiny toes
Let you know that, you don't know
No no, you don't know

Now I've been a father
For twenty one years
And any time I thought
I could hold love
It disappeared, it disappeared

And while I'm thinking
How far I've come
I find I'm back where I started
Oh no, I didn't know

Ten tiny fingers, ten tiny toes
Your daddy's ears and your mummy's nose
That's as far as my knowledge goes
What I see before me are

Ten tiny fingers, ten tiny toes
Let you know that you don't know
No no, you don't know

Hornall Brothers Music Limited

Through Him

I was walking through the middle of the park
On Saturday morning at ten
Looking at the leaves and the bark
Laughing at the dogs and then
A man shoved a pamphlet in my face
All about the forgiveness of sins
I took if from him just in case
I should have thrown it in the bin
Thrown it in the bin
Thrown it in the bin

The pamphlet gave a Belfast address
There was a Scottish name signed on the line
It was the kind of stuff they made me ingest
In school when I was nine
It said "sin is a burden he can lift"
Sin is foul and must be cleansed away
Repent, or you'll be condemned
On the last day, on the last day, on the last day

Thank you so much for sharing
I know it's really caring
To break someone and rebuild them
To break someone and rebuild them
But I'm like the dirty ladies
And all the tiny babies
Who will burn in hell
If they don't come to God through him

Walking through the middle of the park
Saturday morning at ten
Looking at the leaves and the bark
Laughing at the dogs and then

Thank you so much for sharing
I know it's really caring
To break someone and rebuild them
Break em down and then rebuild them

But I'm like those dirty ladies
And all those tiny babies
Who you say will burn in hell
If they don't come to God through him

I was walking through the
middle of the park
On Saturday morning at ten
I was looking at the leaves and
the bark
Laughing at the dogs and then
It was a man shoved a
pamphlet in my face
It was all about the forgiveness
of sins
I took if from him just in case
I should have thrown it in the
bin
Thrown it in the bin
Thrown it in the bin

Hornall Brothers Music Limited

Rainbows and Happy regrets

Leave it alone or it won't get better
You shouldn't touch it at all
If there was a fire and
You tried to use it
It couldn't answer the call
It's like an old man
In a suit of armour
Standing alone in a shed
If I wasn't such a humanitarian
I'd think it better off dead

'Scotland forever' 'Erin Go Bragh'
How may I help you miss?
You bring such a passion to your kiss
You're walking on tiptoes
You don't slurp your tea
The reason is plain to see
You grew up in a house with no TV

Give it some air
And a special cuddle
Don't let it see your concern
You are the judge
Let's have your ruling
It needs some friends
Don't say home schooling
Give it a wipe
Cos now it's drooling
Rainbows and happy regrets

'Scotland forever' 'Erin Go Bragh'
How may I help you miss?
You bring such a passion to your kiss
You're walking on tiptoes
You don't slurp your tea
The reason is plain to see
You grew up in a house with no TV

We live in an age of second chances
Even if they're undeserved
Now it's awake
It heard your calling
Up and away
There is no stalling
Here come those tears
It's loudly bawling
Rainbows and happy regrets

Hornall Brothers Music Limited

Moral Compass

Here we go, one more round
Of an argument you can't lose
And I can't win
And I have to say if I step back
Your points seem stronger than mine yet again
But you hold your truth self-evident
And think that's the wrong place to begin

Elevating principles
To a place where they seem divine

But your moral compass is
Your moral compass is
Your moral compass is not mine

See all those souls
Doing the bad things
Things you believe
You would never do
Well maybe you're right
Or maybe you're just lucky
You haven't lived through
What they've lived through

You have a set of rules
To see you to the grave
Well, that's fine

But your moral compass is
Your moral compass is
Your moral compass is not mine

Your moral compass is
Your moral compass is not mine

Hornall Brothers Music Limited

THE PROCLAIMERS : SHORT BIOGRAPHY - October 2015

After completing a 2-year World tour late in 2013, Craig and Charlie took 2014 off to focus entirely on writing a new album. They headed to Rockfield Studios in December with their band and producer Dave Eringa (Manic Street Preachers, Wilko Johnson & Roger Daltrey, Idlewild, The Who) and recorded their 10th studio album 'Let's Hear It For The Dog's' released by Cooking Vinyl on 27th April this year.

The Proclaimers then returned to the road, touring throughout the UK in 2015 from May through to December with a mammoth run of 70 shows, playing to over 270,000 people. Festivals include Wychwood, T In The Park, Glastonbury Cambridge Folk Festival, Carfest North, Belladrum, Cropredy, V Festivals and Jersey Live.

October sees them embark on their main major city 35-date UK & Ireland tour.

Live plans for 2016 include tours of Australia/New Zealand, Europe, USA and Canada.

April 2013 saw The Proclaimers out on a three week USA acoustic tour before joining up with their live band for a host of UK festivals and concerts over the summer including their fifth Glastonbury appearance, Cornbury, T In The Park, Camp Bestival and a Canadian tour in August. The Proclaimers returned for more UK dates and their final concert this year as the first Scottish band to play at the newly opened Hydro Arena in Glasgow in early October.

1st July saw the release of a thirty-track compilation selected by Craig and Charlie from their 9 studio albums to date. 'The Very Best of The Proclaimers' (25 Years - 1987 to 2012).

Following on from the theatre success of the musical drama featuring songs by The Proclaimers 'Sunshine On Leith', the movie version had its UK release in October (Entertainment Film Distributors) and was hugely popular, opening at number 3, moving up to 2 in it's second and spending another month in the top ten, generating over £4.8 million at the UK Box office. Sunshine On Leith was number 5 in the highest grossing Independent UK films of 2013. The movie was released in the UK on DVD/Blu-ray on 27th January 2014. It has its international releases across the globe throughout 2014 and is released in USA/Canada in 2015.

Screenplay by Stephen Greenhorn, directed by Dexter Fletcher, produced by DNA Films & Black Camel Pictures and starring Peter Mullan, Jane Horrocks, George MacKay, Antonia Thomas, Kevin Guthrie and Freya Mavor.

Strikingly individual, twin brothers Craig and Charlie Reid have over the years enjoyed huge success across the globe as the emotional honesty, political fire, wit and sing-along raucousness of their songs and their extensive touring has enlightened and entertained fans new and old. The Proclaimers have carved out a niche for themselves in the netherworld where pop, folk, new wave and punk collide. In the process they have enjoyed Gold and Platinum singles and albums in UK, USA, Canada, Australia and New Zealand.

Born in Leith in 1962, Craig and Charlie Reid grew up in Edinburgh, Cornwall and Auchtermuchty in Fife. At home, they listened to early rock 'n' roll and country greats such as Jerry Lee Lewis, Merle Haggard and Hank Williams. At school they played in punk bands and formed The Proclaimers in 1983. With a fervent live following growing in Scotland, particularly in Inverness where they performed regularly, their first big break came late in 1986 when they were invited to tour with The Housemartins. Then in January 1987 they made a now seminal appearance on the Channel 4 pop programme The Tube, performing Letter From America & Throw The 'R' Away. Singing in regional accents about Scotland - its emigration and its politics - they were a far cry from the mid-Eighties playlist staples of Rick Astley and Sinitta, and became a phenomenon almost overnight, signing to Chrysalis within a month and recording their debut album acoustically, This Is The Story, a week later, produced by the man who also signed them to Chrysalis, John Williams. Voted NME Readers Best New Band that year, they toured the UK extensively and a new 'band' version of Letter From America, produced by Gerry Rafferty went Top 3 in November.

Complementing their raw, stripped down delivery with the greater musical scope of a full band, they then embraced country and rock on their second album, 1988's Sunshine On Leith produced by Pete Wingfield, which also saw them form their first full live band and go on a 9 month World tour.

In addition to the deeply moving classic title track which has gone on to be an anthem for Hibs fans, the album featured hit singles, the raucous, euphoric I'm Gonna Be (500 Miles) and I'm On My Way. In 1989 'I'm Gonna Be' spent 6 weeks at number 1 in Australia and a was a top 10 college radio hit in USA. The song went on to soar to No. 3 during a 6-month reign in the US Billboard Singles Chart in 1993 after appearing on the soundtrack of the Johnny Depp film Benny And Joon. I'm On My Way also re-emerged in 2001 when it subsequently accompanied one of the pivotal scenes in the hit movie Shrek.

In 1990, The Proclaimers had a huge UK & European hit with their King Of The Road EP. The Proclaimers returned in 1994 with Hit The Highway, an album that featured a three-piece brass section yielding the hit Let's Get Married.

A longer than intended break then ensued before a fourth album, 2001's Persevere, was cut in Minneapolis. Produced by Chris Kimsey with an all star American musician line up, another fantastic collection of Reid/Reid songs re-established The Proclaimers as they went back on another mammoth year long World tour.

Since then, the band have barely stood still, following the 2002 release of their Best Of they continued to tour extensively and one of that year's more unusual highlights saw them perform on the pitch at Hampden Park to over a billion TV viewers before the 2002 UEFA Champions League Final between Real Madrid and Bayer Leverkusen. Two more acclaimed studio albums followed, 2003's Edwyn Collins produced Born Innocent and 2005's more soul orientated Mark Wallis/David Ruffy produced Restless Soul. 2005 saw another live career highpoint, opening the bill at the Live 8 concert at Murrayfield Stadium. 2006 also saw a notable appearance in an episode of Family Guy.

In March 2007, they topped the UK singles chart with a rousing new rendition of their classic anthem I'm Going to Be (500 Miles), a collaboration with comedians Peter Kay and Matt Lucas for Comic Relief, raising over a million pounds for charity in the process. EMI relaunched their 2002 Best Of collection, re-entering the Album Charts at No 5 with sales soaring beyond platinum. September 2007 saw The Proclaimers release their seventh studio album 'Life

With You' (Universal) in the UK to fantastic critical praise and great commercial success. The Proclaimers kicked off their biggest ever UK & Ireland tour in October, 44 dates to over 100,000 fans. In Scotland, they sold more gig tickets than any other single act in 2007.

Touring continued in 2008, with a huge 129 date, yearlong World tour, across Europe, two months coast to coast across the USA & Canada, followed by a variety of shows from Muscat to Bermuda, alongside English seaside resort gigs and European festivals including their fourth Glastonbury appearance and all brought to a triumphant conclusion with a concert at Edinburgh Castle.

In 2009, The Proclaimers released their 8th studio album 'Notes & Rhymes' (Universal) and hit the road for another 95 date World tour. In March, Craig and Charlie headed over to Austin, Texas to make their debut at SXSW where they performed a series of seven acoustic showcases, including a one-off Scottish extravaganza, sharing a bill with Glasvegas and Primal Scream.

Whilst 2010 was spent mainly writing, The Proclaimers performed at 21 summer dates in Europe climaxing with a main stage T In The Park performance.

In October 2011 special editions of The Proclaimers first three albums were released on Chrysalis (This Is The Story, Sunshine On Leith, Hit The Highway), each containing the original album plus a bonus disc containing B-sides, live tracks and previously unreleased radio sessions, all newly remastered at Abbey road Studios, London.

With producer Steve Evans at the helm, The Proclaimers released their 9th studio album 'Like Comedy' in April 2012 to great acclaim by leading independent label Cooking Vinyl. One of their greatest fans, Matt Lucas made his director's debut on the video for the single 'Spinning Around In The Air' where he wrote a script for a Golden wedding anniversary descending into drunken mayhem and in the process managed to persuade Craig and Charlie for a career first, dressing them up as elderly ladies.

The Proclaimers were then back out live with a busy summer in UK which included headlining the Hebridean and Big Tent festivals in Scotland, followed by another headline slot at Cambridge Festival, main stage appearances at the V Festivals in England and three shows at the Singapore Grand Prix. Another unique appearance occurred when The Proclaimers appeared on ITV's Emmerdale – as headliners at Home Farm's music festival, in an episode marking the beginning of the soap's 40th Đbirthday celebrations.

October 2012 saw The Proclaimers head out on an eight week, 36-date UK tour, before finishing the year in style with a Hogmanay concert on the esplanade of Stirling Castle.

The last few years has seen The Proclaimers grace main stages at the likes of V Festival, T In The Park, Isle Of Wight Festival, Womad and Glastonbury in-between regular touring across the globe. Craig and Charlie have reached the rarefied status that few have been able to achieve: with nearly three decades of career longevity, they are as innovative as ever and with every album and show played, they've continued to garner new fans.

Their songs have been used extensively in adverts across the World and the list of movies they have featured in includes The Commitments, The Crossing, Mama's Boy, Bottle Rocket, Benny & Joon, Shrek, Dumb & Dumber, Bye Bye Love, Burke And Hare, The Angel's Share, Bachelorette, Perfect Pitch.

The Proclaimers songs, too, provided the inspiration to an enormously successful, highly acclaimed, award winning new musical, Sunshine On Leith, put together by the Dundee Rep Theatre. Written by Stephen Greenhorn. The drama follows the highs and lows of 2 soldiers returning home from Afghanistan. Families, relationships and life in Leith are not all plain sailing in this exceptional love story about everyday life in Scotland. Directed by James Brining, the musical first toured Scotland in Spring 2007, returning in November 2008 for a 4 month run in Scotland and its first foray into England. The musical had its third outing a 4 month theatre tour (3 months in Scotland, 1 month in England) in Autumn 2010 with the cast for this run starring Billy Boyd, most widely known for playing the Character 'Pippin' in the movies The Lord of The Rings and 'Barret Bondon' in Master and Commander: The Far Side of the World.

Why did it take 20 years before anyone noticed The Proclaimers were born to be turned into a musical? Not since Willy Russell came up with Blood Brothers has Britain produced such a perfect marriage of music and theatre. Had playwright and screenwriter Stephen Greenhorn done nothing else, he should be declared a genius for spotting that the songs of Craig and Charlie Reid - with all their emotional honesty, singalong raucousness and political fire - are a true gift to the stage. THE GUARDIAN

Matt Lucas is a huge fan and in the sleeve notes of their Best Of compilation he writes of Scotland's finest Celtic soul brothers: 'I find it hard to put into words quite how the music of The Proclaimers makes me feel. It makes me laugh. It makes me cry. It just makes me generally euphoric ... Sunshine On Leith says more to me about my life and the way I feel than anything Morrissey or Cobain ever wrote.'

On BBC Radio 4's Desert Island discs, David Tennant describes his first track by The Proclaimers - "I could have chosen any and every track from this band, probably my favourite band of all time. They write the most spectacular songs, big hearted, uncynical passionate songs."

www.proclaimers.co.uk